31. X. 36.

THE WORKS OF

ROBERT LOUIS STEVENSON

TUSITALA EDITION

VOL. XXII

POEMS

VOLUME ONE

A CHILD'S GARDEN OF VERSES
UNDERWOODS
SONGS OF TRAVEL
MORAL EMBLEMS

BY

ROBERT LOUIS STEVENSON

LONDON: WILLIAM HEINEMANN, Ltd:
IN ASSOCIATION WITH CHATTO & WINDUS:
CASSELL & COMPANY, LTD: AND LONGMANS
GREEN & COMPANY.

First Published, TUSITALA EDITION, November, 1923
Second Impression . . . . . . January, 1924
Third Impression . . . . September, 1924
Fourth Impression . . . . . . December, 1924
Fifth Impression . . . . February, 1926
Sixth Impression . . . . September, 1927

PRINTED IN GREAT BRITAIN

CONTENTS

A CHILD'S GARDEN OF VERSES

A*   v

CONTENTS

THE CHILD ALONE

CONTENTS

UNDERWOODS

CONTENTS

PAGE

BOOK II—IN SCOTS

SONGS OF TRAVEL AND OTHER VERSES

CONTENTS

MORAL EMBLEMS

CONTENTS

PREFATORY NOTE

BY MRS. R. L. STEVENSON

DURING all the early part of her married life,
Margaret Stevenson was more or less an invalid,
with persistent and alarming symptoms of consumption ;
her only child, Robert Louis, inherited from her a pre-
disposition to affections of the lungs. He was unfortunate,
besides, in having to endure in infancy the climate of
Edinburgh, which with its cold mists and penetrating
east winds was far from a desirable home for a delicate
child. Unable, through her own ill-health, to take
proper charge of her little son, his mother was forced
to give him over almost entirely into the hands of hired
nurses. The reign of the first nurse was very short, she
being accidentally discovered in a public-house much
the worse for drink, while her tender charge, done up
in a parcel, lay tucked out of sight on a shelf behind the
bar. The second nurse proved no better ; but the third,
Alison Cunningham, familiarly called Cummy, proved
an estimable woman, who soon won the confidence of
the family.

Cummy's piety was her strongest recommendation, but
her convictions and consequent teachings, believing as she
did in a literal hell along with the other tenets of her church,
were rather strong meat for the mental digestion of an
imaginative, nervous child. My husband has told me
of the terrors of the night, when he dared not go to sleep
lest he should wake amid the flames of eternal torment,
and how he would be taken from his bed in the morning unrefreshed, feverish, and ill, but rejoicing that he
had gained at least a respite from what he believed to be
his just doom ; Cummy, kindly soul, never dreaming of

the dire effect of her religious training. The nursery, in the custom of the time, was kept almost hermetically closed, so that not a breath of air could penetrate from the outside ; if little Smoutie, as he was called, waked from his dreams with cries of fright, the watchful Cummy was ready to make him a fresh drink of coffee, which she considered a particularly soothing beverage. According to her lights she was faithful and conscientious, and the child regarded her with the deepest affection.

The terrifying aspects of religion were generally confined to the night hours. In the daytime Cummy, with her contagious gaiety and unceasing inventions for the amusement of her nursling, made the time fly on wings. Her imagination was almost as vivid as the child's, and her tact in his management was unfailing. She had a great feeling for poetry and the music of words, and can still tell a story with much dramatic effect. When the sick child turned from his food and would not eat, Cummy could usually persuade him to another effort by saying, " It is made from the finest of the wheat." The biblical words " shew bread " might also be used when everything else failed, but I fancy Cummy was chary of quoting from the sacred book unless the occasion were very serious indeed.

Had my husband's infancy been passed in the fresh air and sunshine of a milder climate, his whole life might have been different. His choice of the profession of literature was an acknowledgment that his health would not admit of his becoming what he wished to be most,—a soldier. To be sure, the child often visited Colinton Manse, where the grandchildren of Dr. Balfour were more than welcome. To question the healthfulness of Colinton would be like a heresy in the family, but it lies on low, damp ground, and in any other part of the world would suggest malaria. No doubt, too, the minister's little grandson would be carefully dressed to befit his position, and not allowed the freedom that would have been so wholesome for him.

Judged by the standards of to-day, the methods of

the medical profession were inconceivably harsh and
ignorant, and it seems a miracle that my husband should
have survived their treatment and grown to manhood.
When the little Louis was stricken with gastric fever
he was dosed with powerful drugs; no one thought of
looking into the sanitary condition of the premises, which
were afterwards found to have been for years in a most
dangerous state. And when the child, weakened by an
attack of pneumonia, took cold after cold, antimonial
wine was administered continuously for a period extend-
ing into months; "enough," said Dr. George Balfour,
"to ruin his constitution for life." No wonder that
after a little time at play he became so feverishly excited
that his toys must be removed and his playmates sent
away.

My husband drew upon his memory for *The Sick Child*
who lay awake hoping for the dawn, and listening for the
sound of the morning carts that proved the weary night
was almost over. Indeed, every poem in *The Child's Garden*
was a bit out of his own childhood. He had little understand-
ing of children in general; I remember his watching with
puzzled amazement the games of a little brother and sister
who were visiting us at Bournemouth. Their poverty of
resource, and the spiritless way they went about their
sport, were most distressing to him. When he found that
they were not exceptional, but represented a pretty fair
average, he exclaimed: "I see the approaching decline
of England! There is something radically wrong in a
generation that does not know how to play." I imagine,
however, that it requires something almost like genius to
play as he played, and that it was hardly fair to judge
our little guests from the plane of his own childhood.

In spite of the many days and nights passed in the
"Land of Counterpane," and shining, perhaps, all the
brighter by comparison, there were brilliant episodes of
play that remained clearer in my husband's memory than
almost any other part of his life. He was especially
happy in the companionship of two of his Edinburgh
cousins,—Willie and Henrietta Traquair. As a little

girl, Henrietta already showed the characteristics that
were her charm in womanhood. Never quarrelsome,
and always cheerfully willing to take a secondary place, she
nevertheless made her individuality felt, and threw a
romantic glamour over every part she assumed. Even the
wicked ogre, or giant, she endowed with unexpected attri-
butes of generosity, and her impersonation of a chivalrous
knight was ideal. When I last saw Henrietta, a few
years ago, we both knew that she had but a little while
to live, but the undaunted light in her eyes seemed to say :—

> " Must we to bed, indeed? Well then
> Let us arise and go like men."

From the memory of these early days my husband
plucked a blossom here and there for *The Child's Garden*.
A beginning was made by the writing of a few verses while
we stopped in Braemar. A few months later, in Hyères,
the games of his childhood served in a new way again to
interest and amuse him. After a terrible hemorrhage, he
fell a victim to sciatica, and at the same time was tem-
porarily blind from an attack of ophthalmia. Not only
was all light excluded from the room where he lay, but
on account of the hemorrhage his right arm was closely
bound to his side. Most men would have succumbed
to the force of circumstances, but he, undismayed,
determined to circumvent the fate he would not accept.
Across his bed a board was laid on which large sheets
of paper were pinned ; on these, or on a slate fastened
to the board, he laboriously wrote out in the darkness,
with his left hand, many more of the songs of his childhood. In 1885 these were collected in a volume first
called *Penny Whistles*, but afterwards changed to *A Child's
Garden of Verses*, and published under that name with
the addition of six envoys.

F. V. DE G. S.

For the long nights you lay awake
And watched for my unworthy sake:
For your most comfortable hand
That led me through the uneven land:
For all the story-books you read:
For all the pains you comforted:
For all you pitied, all you bore,
In sad and happy days of yore:—
My second Mother, my first Wife,
The angel of my infant life—
From the sick child, now well and old,
Take, nurse, the little book you hold!

And grant it, Heaven, that all who read
May find as dear a nurse at need,
And every child who lists my rhyme,
In the bright, fireside, nursery clime,
May hear it in as kind a voice
As made my childish days rejoice!

R. L. S.

TO

ALISON CUNNINGHAM
FROM HER NURSE

For the long nights you lay awake
And watched for my unworthy sake:
For your most comfortable hand
That led me through the uneven land:
For all the story-books you read:
For all the pains you comforted:
For all you pitied, all you bore,
In sad and happy days of yore:—
My second Mother, my first Wife,
The angel of my infant life—
From the sick child, now well and old,
Take, nurse, the little book you hold!

And grant it, Heaven, that all who read
May find as dear a nurse at need,
And every child who lists my rhyme,
In the bright, fireside, nursery clime,
May hear it in as kind a voice
As made my childish days rejoice!

R. L. S.

A CHILD'S GARDEN
OF VERSES

A Child's Garden of Verses
was first published in 1885

A CHILD'S GARDEN OF VERSES

I

BED IN SUMMER

In winter I get up at night
And dress by yellow candle-light.
In summer, quite the other way,
I have to go to bed by day.

I have to go to bed and see
The birds still hopping on the tree,
Or hear the grown-up people's feet
Still going past me in the street.

And does it not seem hard to you,
When all the sky is clear and blue,
And I should like so much to play,
To have to go to bed by day?

II

A THOUGHT

It is very nice to think
The world is full of meat and drink,
With little children saying grace
In every Christian kind of place.

III

AT THE SEA-SIDE

When I was down beside the sea,
A wooden spade they gave to me
    To dig the sandy shore.

My holes were empty like a cup,
In every hole the sea came up,
Till it could come no more.

IV.

YOUNG NIGHT THOUGHT

ALL night long, and every night,
When my mamma puts out the light,
I see the people marching by,
As plain as day, before my eye

Armies and emperors and kings,
All carrying different kinds of things,
And marching in so grand a way,
You never saw the like by day.

So fine a show was never seen
At the great circus on the green ;
For every kind of beast and man
Is marching in that caravan.

At first they move a little slow,
But still the faster on they go,
And still beside them close I keep
Until we reach the town of Sleep.

V

WHOLE DUTY OF CHILDREN

A CHILD should always say what's true,
And speak when he is spoken to,
And behave mannerly at table :
At least as far as he is able.

VI
RAIN

THE rain is raining all around,
    It falls on field and tree,
It rains on the umbrellas here,
    And on the ships at sea.

VII
PIRATE STORY

THREE of us afloat in the meadow by the swing,
    Three of us aboard in the basket on the lea.
Winds are in the air, they are blowing in the spring,
    And waves are on the meadows like the waves there are
        at sea.

Where shall we adventure, to-day that we're afloat,
    Wary of the weather and steering by a star?
Shall it be to Africa, a-steering of the boat,
    To Providence, or Babylon, or off to Malabar?

Hi! but here's a squadron a-rowing on the sea—
    Cattle on the meadow a-charging with a roar!
Quick, and we'll escape them, they're as mad as they can
        be,
    The wicket is the harbour and the garden is the shore.

VIII
FOREIGN LANDS

UP into the cherry-tree
Who should climb but little me?
I held the trunk with both my hands
And looked abroad on foreign lands.

I saw the next-door garden lie,
Adorned with flowers, before my eye,
And many pleasant places more
That I had never seen before.

I saw the dimpling river pass
And be the sky's blue looking-glass;
The dusty roads go up and down
With people tramping in to town.

If I could find a higher tree,
Farther and farther I should see,
To where the grown-up river slips
Into the sea among the ships,

To where the roads on either hand
Lead onward into fairy land,
Where all the children dine at five,
And all the playthings come alive.

IX

WINDY NIGHTS

WHENEVER the moon and stars are set,
  Whenever the wind is high,
All night long in the dark and wet,
  A man goes riding by.
Late in the night when the fires are out,
Why does he gallop and gallop about?

Whenever the trees are crying aloud,
  And ships are tossed at sea,
By, on the highway, low and loud,
  By at the gallop goes he.
By at the gallop he goes, and then
By he comes back at the gallop again.

X
TRAVEL

I SHOULD like to rise and go
Where the golden apples grow ;—
Where below another sky
Parrot islands anchored lie,
And, watched by cockatoos and goats,
Lonely Crusoes building boats ;—
Where in sunshine reaching out
Eastern cities, miles about,
Are with mosque and minaret
Among sandy gardens set,
And the rich goods from near and far
Hang for sale in the bazaar ;—
Where the Great Wall round China goes,
And on one side the desert blows,
And with bell and voice and drum,
Cities on the other hum ;—
Where are forests, hot as fire,
Wide as England, tall as a spire,
Full of apes and cocoa-nuts
And the negro hunters' huts ;—
Where the knotty crocodile
Lies and blinks in the Nile,
And the red flamingo flies
Hunting fish before his eyes ;—
Where in jungles, near and far,
Man-devouring tigers are,
Lying close and giving ear
Lest the hunt be drawing near,
Or a comer-by be seen
Swinging in a palanquin ;—
Where among the desert sands
Some deserted city stands,
All its children, sweep and prince,
Grown to manhood ages since,
Not a foot in street or house,
Not a stir of child or mouse

And when kindly falls the night,
In all the town no spark of light.
There I'll come when I'm a man
With a camel caravan ;
Light a fire in the gloom
Of some dusty dining-room ;
See the pictures on the walls,
Heroes, fights, and festivals ;
And in a corner find the toys
Of the old Egyptian boys.

XI

SINGING

OF speckled eggs the birdie sings
    And nests among the trees ;
The sailor sings of ropes and things
    In ships upon the seas.

The children sing in far Japan,
    The children sing in Spain ;
The organ with the organ man
    Is singing in the rain.

XII

LOOKING FORWARD

WHEN I am grown to man's estate
I shall be very proud and great,
And tell the other girls and boys
Not to meddle with my toys.

XIII

A GOOD PLAY

WE built a ship upon the stairs
All made of the back-bedroom chairs,
And filled it full of sofa pillows
To go a-sailing on the billows.

We took a saw and several nails,
And water in the nursery pails ;
And Tom said, " Let us also take
An apple and a slice of cake ; "—
Which was enough for Tom and me
To go a-sailing on, till tea.

We sailed along for days and days,
And had the very best of plays ;
But Tom fell out and hurt his knee,
So there was no one left but me.

XIV

WHERE GO THE BOATS ?

DARK brown is the river,
    Golden is the sand.
It flows along for ever,
    With trees on either hand.

Green leaves a-floating,
    Castles of the foam,
Boats of mine a-boating—
    Where will all come home ?

On goes the river
    And out past the mill,
Away down the valley,
    Away down the hill.

Away down the river,
    A hundred miles or more,
Other little children
    Shall bring my boats ashore.

XV

AUNTIE'S SKIRTS

WHENEVER Auntie moves around,
Her dresses make a curious sound ;
They trail behind her up the floor,
And trundle after through the door.

XVI

THE LAND OF COUNTERPANE

WHEN I was sick and lay a-bed,
I had two pillows at my head,
And all my toys beside me lay
To keep me happy all the day.

And sometimes for an hour or so
I watched my leaden soldiers go,
With different uniforms and drills,
Among the bed-clothes, through the hills;

And sometimes sent my ships in fleets
All up and down among the sheets;
Or brought my trees and houses out,
And planted cities all about.

I was the giant great and still
That sits upon the pillow-hill,
And sees before him, dale and plain,
The pleasant land of counterpane.

XVII

THE LAND OF NOD

FROM breakfast on all through the day
At home among my friends I stay;
But every night I go abroad
Afar into the land of Nod.

All by myself I have to go,
With none to tell me what to do—
All alone beside the streams
And up the mountain-sides of dreams.

The strangest things are there for me,
Both things to eat and things to see,
And many frightening sights abroad
Till morning in the land of Nod.

Try as I like to find the way,
I never can get back by day,
Nor can remember plain and clear
The curious music that I hear.

XVIII

MY SHADOW

I HAVE a little shadow that goes in and out with me,
And what can be the use of him is more than I can see.
He is very, very like me from the heels up to the head ;
And I see him jump before me, when I jump into my
   bed.

The funniest thing about him is the way he likes to grow—
Not at all like proper children, which is always very slow ;
For he sometimes shoots up taller like an india-rubber
   ball,
And he sometimes gets so little that there's none of him
   at all.

He hasn't got a notion of how children ought to play,
And can only make a fool of me in every sort of way.
He stays so close beside me, he's a coward you can see ;
I'd think shame to stick to nursie as that shadow sticks
   to me !

One morning, very early, before the sun was up,
I rose and found the shining dew on every buttercup ;
But my lazy little shadow, like an arrant sleepy-head,
Had stayed at home behind me and was fast asleep in bed.

XIX
SYSTEM

EVERY night my prayers I say,
And get my dinner every day;
And every day that I've been good,
I get an orange after food.

The child that is not clean and neat,
With lots of toys and things to eat,
He is a naughty child, I'm sure—
Or else his dear papa is poor.

XX
A GOOD BOY

I WOKE before the morning, I was happy all the day,
I never said an ugly word, but smiled and stuck to play.

And now at last the sun is going down behind the wood,
And I am very happy, for I know that I've been good.

My bed is waiting cool and fresh, with linen smooth and
    fair,
And I must off to sleepsin-by, and not forget my prayer.

I know that, till to-morrow I shall see the sun arise,
No ugly dream shall fright my mind, no ugly sight my
    eyes.

But slumber hold me tightly till I waken in the dawn,
And hear the thrushes singing in the lilacs round the lawn.

XXI
ESCAPE AT BEDTIME

THE lights from the parlour and kitchen shone out
    Through the blinds and the windows and bars;
And high overhead and all moving about,
    There were thousands of millions of stars.

There ne'er were such thousands of leaves on a tree,
  Nor of people in church or the Park,
As the crowds of the stars that looked down upon me,
  And that glittered and winked in the dark.
The Dog, and the Plough, and the Hunter, and all.
  And the star of the sailor, and Mars,
These shone in the sky, and the pail by the wall
  Would be half full of water and stars.
They saw me at last, and they chased me with cries,
  And they soon had me packed into bed ;
But the glory kept shining and bright in my eyes,
  And the stars going round in my head.

XXII

MARCHING SONG

Bring the comb and play upon it !
  Marching, here we come !
Willie cocks his Highland bonnet,
  Johnnie beats the drum.

Mary Jane commands the party,
  Peter leads the rear ;
Feet in time, alert and hearty,
  Each a Grenadier !

All in the most martial manner
  Marching double-quick ;
While the napkin like a banner
  Waves upon the stick !

Here's enough of fame and pillage,
  Great commander Jane !
Now that we've been round the village,
  Let's go home again.

XXIII

THE COW

THE friendly cow, all red and white,
    I love with all my heart:
She gives me cream with all her might,
    To eat with apple-tart.

She wanders lowing here and there,
    And yet she cannot stray,
All in the pleasant open air,
    The pleasant light of day;

And blown by all the winds that pass,
    And wet with all the showers,
She walks among the meadow grass
    And eats the meadow flowers.

XXIV

HAPPY THOUGHT

THE world is so full of a number of things,
I'm sure we should all be as happy as kings.

XXV

THE WIND

I SAW you toss the kites on high
And blow the birds about the sky;
And all around I heard you pass,
Like ladies' skirts across the grass—
    O wind, a-blowing all day long,
    O wind, that sings so loud a song!

I saw the different things you did,
But always you yourself you hid.
I felt you push, I heard you call,
I could not see yourself at all—
    O wind, a-blowing all day long,
    O wind, that sings so loud a song!

O you that are so strong and cold,
O blower, are you young or old?
Are you a beast of field and tree,
Or just a stronger child than me?
    O wind, a-blowing all day long,
    O wind, that sings so loud a song!

XXVI

KEEPSAKE MILL

OVER the borders, a sin without pardon,
  Breaking the branches and crawling below,
Out through the breach in the wall of the garden,
  Down by the banks of the river, we go.

Here is the mill with the humming of thunder,
  Here is the weir with the wonder of foam,
Here is the sluice with the race running under—
  Marvellous places, though handy to home!

Sounds of the village grow stiller and stiller,
  Stiller the note of the birds on the hill;
Dusty and dim are the eyes of the miller,
  Deaf are his ears with the moil of the mill.

Years may go by, and the wheel in the river
  Wheel as it wheels for us, children, to-day,
Wheel and keep roaring and foaming for ever,
  Long after all of the boys are away.

Home from the Indies, and home from the ocean,
  Heroes and soldiers we all shall come home;
Still we shall find the old mill-wheel in motion,
  Turning and churning that river to foam.

You with the bean that I gave when we quarrelled,
  I with your marble of Saturday last,
Honoured and old and all gaily apparelled,
  Here we shall meet and remember the past

XXVII

GOOD AND BAD CHILDREN

CHILDREN, you are very little,
And your bones are very brittle;
If you would grow great and stately,
You must try to walk sedately.

You must still be bright and quite,
And content with simple diet;
And remain, through all bewild'ring,
Innocent and honest children.

Happy hearts and happy faces,
Happy play in grassy places—
That was how, in ancient ages,
Children grew to kings and sages.

But the unkind and the unruly,
And the sort who eat unduly,
They must never hope for glory—
Theirs is quite a different story!

Cruel children, crying babies,
All grow up as geese and gabies,
Hated, as their age increases,
By their nephews and their nieces.

XXVIII

FOREIGN CHILDREN

LITTLE Indian, Sioux or Crow,
Little frosty Eskimo,
Little Turk or Japanee,
O! don't you wish that you were me?

You have seen the scarlet trees
And the lions over seas;
You have eaten ostrich eggs,
And turned the turtles off their legs.

Such a life is very fine,
But it's not so nice as mine :
You must often, as you trod,
Have wearied *not* to be abroad.

You have curious things to eat,
I am fed on proper meat ;
You must dwell beyond the foam,
But I am safe and live at home.

Little Indian, Sioux or Crow,
Little frosty Eskimo,
Little Turk or Japanee,
O ! don't you wish that you were me ?

XXIX
THE SUN'S TRAVELS

THE sun is not a-bed when I
At night upon my pillow lie ;
Still round the earth his way he takes,
And morning after morning makes.

While here at home, in shining day,
We round the sunny garden play,
Each little Indian sleepy-head
Is being kissed and put to bed.

And when at eve I rise from tea,
Day dawns beyond the Atlantic Sea,
And all the children in the West
Are getting up and being dressed.

XXX
THE LAMPLIGHTER

My tea is nearly ready and the sun has left the sky ;
It's time to take the window to see Leerie going by ;
For every night at tea-time and before you take your seat,
With lantern and with ladder he comes posting up the street.

Now Tom would be a driver and Maria go to sea,
And my papa's a banker and as rich as he can be ;
But I, when I am stronger and can choose what I'm to do,
O Leerie, I'll go round at night and light the lamps with you !

For we are very lucky, with a lamp before the door,
And Leerie stops to light it as he lights so many more ;
And O ! before you hurry by with ladder and with light,
O Leerie, see a little child and nod to him to-night !

XXXI
MY BED IS A BOAT

My bed is like a little boat ;
　　Nurse helps me in when I embark ;
She girds me in my sailor's coat
　　And starts me in the dark.

At night, I go on board and say
　　Good-night to all my friends on shore ;
I shut my eyes and sail away
　　And see and hear no more.

And sometimes things to bed I take,
　　As prudent sailors have to do ;
Perhaps a slice of wedding-cake,
　　Perhaps a toy or two.

All night across the dark we steer :
　　But when the day returns at last,
Safe in my room, beside the pier,
　　I find my vessel fast.

XXXII
THE MOON

The moon has a face like the clock in the hall ;
She shines on thieves on the garden wall,
On streets and fields and harbour quays,
And birdies asleep in the forks of the trees.

The squalling cat and the squeaking mouse,
The howling dog by the door of the house,
The bat that lies in bed at noon,
All love to be out by the light of the moon

But all of the things that belong to the day
Cuddle to sleep to be out of her way ;
And flowers and children close their eyes
Till up in the morning the sun shall rise.

XXXIII

THE SWING

How do you like to go up in a swing,
     Up in the air so blue ?
Oh, I do think it the pleasantest thing
     Ever a child can do !

Up in the air and over the wall,
     Till I can see so wide,
Rivers and trees and cattle and all
     Over the countryside—

Till I look down on the garden green,
     Down on the roof so brown—
Up in the air I go flying again,
     Up in the air and down !

XXXIV

TIME TO RISE

A BIRDIE with a yellow bill
Hopped upon the window sill,
Cocked his shining eye and said :
" Ain't vou 'shamed, you sleepy-head ! "

XXXV

LOOKING-GLASS RIVER

SMOOTH it slides upon its travel,
　　Here a wimple, there a gleam—
　　　O the clean gravel!
　　　O the smooth stream!

Sailing blossoms, silver fishes,
　　Paven pools as clear as air—
　　　How a child wishes
　　　To live down there!

We can see our coloured faces
　　Floating on the shaken pool
　　　Down in cool places,
　　　Dim and very cool;

Till a wind or water wrinkle,
　　Dipping marten, plumping trout,
　　　Spreads in a twinkle
　　　And blots all out.

See the rings pursue each other;
　　All below grows black as night,
　　　Just as if mother
　　　Had blown out the light!

Patience, children, just a minute—
　　See the spreading circles die;
　　　The stream and all in it
　　　Will clear by-and-by.

XXXVI

FAIRY BREAD

COME up here, O dusty feet!
Here is fairy bread to eat.
Here in my retiring room,
Children, you may dine

On the golden smell of broom
  And the shade of pine ;
And when you have eaten well,
Fairy stories hear and tell.

XXXVII

FROM A RAILWAY CARRIAGE

FASTER than fairies, faster than witches,
Bridges and houses, hedges and ditches ;
And charging along like troops in a battle,
All through the meadows the horses and cattle :
All of the sights of the hill and the plain
Fly as thick as driving rain ;
And ever again, in the wink of an eye,
Painted stations whistle by.

Here is a child who clambers and scrambles,
All by himself and gathering brambles ;
Here is a tramp who stands and gazes ;
And there is the green for stringing the daisies !
Here is a cart run away in the road
Lumping along with man and load ;
And here is a mill, and there is a river :
Each a glimpse and gone for ever !

XXXVIII

WINTER-TIME

LATE lies the wintry sun a-bed,
A frosty, fiery sleepy-head ;
Blinks but an hour or two ; and then,
A blood-red orange, sets again.

Before the stars have left the skies,
At morning in the dark I rise;
And shivering in my nakedness,
By the cold candle, bathe and dress.

Close by the jolly fire I sit
To warm my frozen bones a bit;
Or with a reindeer-sled, explore
The colder countries round the door.

When, to go out, my nurse doth wrap
Me in my comforter and cap,
The cold wind burns my face, and blows
Its frosty pepper up my nose.

Black are my steps on silver sod;
Thick blows my frosty breath abroad;
And tree and house, and hill and lake,
Are frosted like a wedding-cake.

XXXIX

THE HAYLOFT

THROUGH all the pleasant meadow-side
    The grass grew shoulder-high,
Till the shining scythes went far and wide
    And cut it down to dry.

These green and sweetly smelling crops
    They led in waggons home;
And they piled them here in mountain tops
    For mountaineers to roam.

Here is Mount Clear, Mount Rusty-Nail,
    Mount Eagle and Mount High;—
The mice that in these mountains dwell
    No happier are than I!

O what a joy to clamber there,
  O what a place for play,
With the sweet, the dim, the dusty air,
  The happy hills of hay.

XL

FAREWELL TO THE FARM

THE coach is at the door at last ;
The eager children, mounting fast
And kissing hands, in chorus sing :
Good-bye, good-bye, to everything !

To house and garden, field and lawn,
The meadow-gates we swang upon,
To pump and stable, tree and swing,
Good-bye, good-bye, to everything !

And fare you well for evermore,
O ladder at the hayloft door,
O hayloft where the cobwebs cling,
Good-bye, good-bye, to everything !

Crack goes the whip, and off we go ;
The trees and houses smaller grow ;
Last, round the woody turn we swing ;
Good-bye, good-bye, to everything !

XLI

NORTH-WEST PASSAGE

1. GOOD NIGHT

WHEN the bright lamp is carried in,
The sunless hours again begin ;
O'er all without, in field and lane,
The haunted night returns again.

Now we behold the embers flee
About the firelit hearth ; and see
Our faces painted as we pass,
Like pictures, on the window-glass.

Must we to bed indeed ? Well then,
Let us arise and go like men,
And face with an undaunted tread
The long black passage up to bed.

Farewell, O brother, sister, sire !
O pleasant party round the fire !
The songs you sing, the tales you tell,
Till far to-morrow, fare ye well !

2. SHADOW MARCH

All round the house is the jet-black night ;
    It stares through the window-pane ;
It crawls in the corners, hiding from the light,
    And it moves with the moving flame.

Now my little heart goes a-beating like a drum,
    With the breath of the Bogie in my hair ;
And all round the candle the crooked shadows
        come
    And go marching along up the stair.

The shadow of the balusters, the shadow of the
        lamp,
    The shadow of the child that goes to bed—
All the wicked shadows coming, tramp, tramp,
        tramp,
    With the black night overhead.

3. IN PORT

Last, to the chamber where I lie
My fearful footsteps patter nigh,
And come from out the cold and gloom
Into my warm and cheerful room.

There, safe arrived, we turn about
To keep the coming shadows out,
And close the happy door at last
On all the perils that we passed.

Then, when mamma goes by to bed,
She shall come in with tip-toe tread,
And see me lying warm and fast
And in the Land of Nod at last.

THE CHILD ALONE

I

THE UNSEEN PLAYMATE

WHEN children are playing alone on the green,
In comes the playmate that never was seen.
When children are happy and lonely and good,
The Friend of the Children comes out of the wood

Nobody heard him and nobody saw,
His is a picture you never could draw,
But he's sure to be present, abroad or at home,
When children are happy and playing alone.

He lies in the laurels, he runs on the grass,
He sings when you tinkle the musical glass;
Whene'er you are happy and cannot tell why,
The Friend of the Children is sure to be by !

He loves to be little, he hates to be big,
'Tis he that inhabits the caves that you dig;
'Tis he when you play with your soldiers of tin
That sides with the Frenchmen and never can win.

'Tis he, when at night you go off to your bed,
Bids you go to your sleep and not trouble your head;
For wherever they're lying, in cupboard or shelf,
'Tis he will take care of your playthings himself !

II

MY SHIP AND I

O IT's I that am the captain of a tidy little ship,
    Of a ship that goes a-sailing on the pond;
And my ship it keeps a-turning all around and all about,
But when I'm a little older, I shall find the secret out
    How to send my vessel sailing on beyond.

For I mean to grow as little as the dolly at the helm,
And the dolly I intend to come alive;
And with him beside to help me, it's a-sailing I shall go,
It's a-sailing on the water, when the jolly breezes blow
And the vessel goes a divie-divie-dive.

O it's then you'll see me sailing through the rushes and
the reeds,
And you'll hear the water singing at the prow;
For beside the dolly sailor, I'm to voyage and explore,
To land upon the island where no dolly was before,
And to fire the penny cannon in the bow.

III

MY KINGDOM

Down by a shining water well
I found a very little dell,
  No higher than my head.
The heather and the gorse about
In summer bloom were coming out,
  Some yellow and some red.

I called the little pool a sea;
The little hills were big to me;
  For I am very small.
I made a boat, I made a town,
I searched the caverns up and down,
  And named them one and all.

And all about was mine, I said,
The little sparrows overhead,
  The little minnows too.
This was the world and I was king;
For me the bees came by to sing,
  For me the swallows flew.

I played there were no deeper seas,
Nor any wider plains than these,
    Nor other kings than me.
At last I heard my mother call
Out from the house at even-fall,
    To call me home to tea.

And I must rise and leave my dell,
And leave my dimpled water well,
    And leave my heather blooms.
Alas ! and as my home I neared,
How very big my nurse appeared,
    How great and cool the rooms !

IV

PICTURE-BOOKS IN WINTER

SUMMER fading, winter comes—
Frosty mornings, tingling thumbs,
Window robins, winter rooks,
And the picture story-books.

Water now is turned to stone
Nurse and I can walk upon ;
Still we find the flowing brooks
In the picture story-books.

All the pretty things put by,
Wait upon the children's eye,
Sheep and shepherds, trees and crooks
In the picture story-books.

We may see how all things are,
Seas and cities, near and far,
And the flying fairies' looks,
In the picture story-books.

How am I to sing your praise,
Happy chimney-corner days,
Sitting safe in nursery nooks,
Reading picture story-books ?

V

MY TREASURES

THESE nuts, that I keep in the back of the nest
Where all my lead soldiers are lying at rest,
Were gathered in autumn by nursie and me
In a wood with a well by the side of the sea.

This whistle we made (and how clearly it sounds !)
By the side of a field at the end of the grounds.
Of a branch of a plane, with a knife of my own,
It was nursie who made it, and nursie alone !

The stone, with the white and the yellow and grey,
We discovered I cannot tell *how* far away ;
And I carried it back although weary and cold,
For, though father denies it, I'm sure it is gold.

But of all my treasures the last is the king,
For there's very few children possess such a thing ;
And that is a chisel, both handle and blade,
Which a man who was really a carpenter made.

VI

BLOCK CITY

WHAT are you able to build with your blocks ?
Castles and palaces, temples and docks.
Rain may keep raining, and others go roam,
But I can be happy and building at home.

Let the sofa be mountains, the carpet be sea,
There I'll establish a city for me :
A kirk and a mill and a palace beside,
And a harbour as well where my vessels may ride.

Great is the palace with pillar and wall,
A sort of a tower on the top of it all,
And steps coming down in an orderly way
To where my toy vessels lie safe in the bay.

This one is sailing and that one is moored :
Hark to the song of the sailors on board !
And see on the steps of my palace, the kings
Coming and going with presents and things !

Now I have done with it, down let it go !
All in a moment the town is laid low.
Block upon block lying scattered and free,
What is there left of my town by the sea ?

Yet as I saw it, I see it again,
The kirk and the palace, the ships and the men,
And as long as I live, and where'er I may be,
I'll always remember my town by the sea.

VII

THE LAND OF STORY-BOOKS

AT evening when the lamp is lit,
Around the fire my parents sit ;
They sit at home and talk and sing,
And do not play at anything.

Now, with my little gun, I crawl
All in the dark along the wall,
And follow round the forest track
Away behind the sofa back.

There, in the night, where none can spy,
All in my hunter's camp I lie,
And play at books that I have read
Till it is time to go to bed.

These are the hills, these are the woods,
These are my starry solitudes ;
And there the river by whose brink
The roaring lions come to drink.

I see the others far away
As if in firelit camp they lay,
And I, like to an Indian scout,
Around their party prowled about.

So, when my nurse comes in for me,
Home I return across the sea,
And go to bed with backward looks
At my dear land of Story-books.

VIII

ARMIES IN THE FIRE

THE lamps now glitter down the street ;
Faintly sound the falling feet ;
And the blue even slowly falls
About the garden trees and walls.

Now in the falling of the gloom
The red fire paints the empty room :
And warmly on the roof it looks,
And flickers on the backs of books.

Armies march by tower and spire
Of cities blazing, in the fire ;—
Till as I gaze with staring eyes,
The armies fade, the lustre dies.

Then once again the glow returns ;
Again the phantom city burns ;
And down the red-hot valley, lo !
The phantom armies marching go !

Blinking embers, tell me true
Where are those armies marching to,
And what the burning city is
That crumbles in your furnaces !

IX

THE LITTLE LAND

WHEN at home alone I sit
And am very tired of it,
I have just to shut my eyes
To go sailing through the skies—
To go sailing far away
To the pleasant Land of Play ;
To the fairy land afar
Where the Little People are ;
Where the clover-tops are trees,
And the rain-pools are the seas,
And the leaves like little ships
Sail about on tiny trips ;
And above the daisy tree
    Through the grasses,
High o'erhead the Bumble Bee
    Hums and passes.

In that forest to and fro
I can wander, I can go ;
See the spider and the fly,
And the ants go marching by
Carrying parcels with their feet
Down the green and grassy street.
I can in the sorrel sit
Where the ladybird alit.
I can climb the jointed grass ;
    And on high
See the greater swallows pass
    In the sky,
And the round sun rolling by
Heeding no such things as I.

Through that forest I can pass
Till, as in a looking-glass,
Humming fly and daisy tree
And my tiny self I see,
Painted very clear and neat
On the rain-pool at my feet.
Should a leaflet come to land
Drifting near to where I stand,
Straight I'll board that tiny boat
Round the rain-pool sea to float.

Little thoughtful creatures sit
On the grassy coasts of it ;
Little things with lovely eyes
See me sailing with surprise.
Some are clad in armour green—
(These have sure to battle been !)—
Some are pied with ev'ry hue,
Black and crimson, gold and blue ;
Some have wings and swift are gone ;—
But they all look kindly on.

When my eyes I once again
Open, and see all things plain :
High bare walls, great bare floor ;
Great big knobs on drawer and door ;
Great big people perched on chairs,
Stitching tucks and mending tears,
Each a hill that I could climb,
And talking nonsense all the time—
        O dear me,
        That I could be
A sailor on the rain-pool sea,
A climber in the clover tree,
And just come back, a sleepy-head,
Late at night to go to bed.

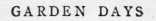

GARDEN DAYS

I

NIGHT AND DAY

WHEN the golden day is done,
  Through the closing portal,
Child and garden, flower and sun,
  Vanish all things mortal.

As the blinding shadows fall,
  As the rays diminish,
Under evening's cloak, they all
  Roll away and vanish.

Garden darkened, daisy shut,
  Child in bed, they slumber—
Glow-worm in the highway rut,
  Mice among the lumber.

In the darkness houses shine,
  Parents move with candles;
Till on all the night divine
  Turns the bedroom handles.

Till at last the day begins
  In the east a-breaking,
In the hedges and the whins
  Sleeping birds a-waking.

In the darkness shapes of things,
  Houses, trees, and hedges,
Clearer grow; and sparrows' wings
  Beat on window ledges.

These shall wake the yawning maid;
  She the door shall open—
Finding dew on garden glade
  And the morning broken.

There my garden grows again
  Green and rosy painted,
As at eve behind the pane
  From my eyes it fainted.

Just as it was shut away,
  Toy-like, in the even,
Here I see it glow with day,
  Under glowing heaven.

Every path and every plot,
  Every bush of roses,
Every blue forget-me-not
  Where the dew reposes.

" Up ! " they cry, " the day is come
  On the smiling valleys :
We have beat the morning drum ;
  Playmate, join your allies ! "

II
NEST EGGS

BIRDS all the sunny day
  Flutter and quarrel,
Here in the arbour-like
  Tent of the laurel.

Here in the fork
  The brown nest is seated ;
Four little blue eggs
  The mother keeps heated.

While we stand watching her,
  Staring like gabies,
Safe in each egg are the
  Bird's little babies.

Soon the frail eggs they shall
   Chip, and upspringing
Make all the April woods
   Merry with singing.

Younger than we are,
   O children, and frailer,
Soon in blue air they'll be
   Singer and sailor.

We, so much older,
   Taller and stronger,
We shall look down on the
   Birdies no longer.

They shall go flying
   With musical speeches
High overhead in the
   Tops of the beeches.

In spite of our wisdom
   And sensible talking,
We on our feet must go
   Plodding and walking.

III

THE FLOWERS

ALL the names I know from nurse :
Gardener's garters, Shepherd's purse,
Bachelor's buttons, Lady's smock,
And the Lady Hollyhock.

Fairy places, fairy things,
Fairy woods where the wild bee wings,
Tiny trees for tiny dames—
These must all be fairy names !

Tiny woods below whose boughs
Shady fairies weave a house ;
Tiny tree-tops, rose or thyme,
Where the braver fairies climb !

Fair are grown-up people's trees,
But the fairest woods are these ;
Where if I were not so tall,
I should live for good and all.

IV
SUMMER SUN

GREAT is the sun, and wide he goes
Through empty heaven without repose ;
And in the blue and glowing days
More thick than rain he showers his rays.

Though closer still the blinds we pull
To keep the shady parlour cool,
Yet he will find a chink or two
To slip his golden fingers through.

The dusty attic, spider-clad,
He, through the keyhole, maketh glad ;
And through the broken edge of tiles,
Into the laddered hayloft smiles.

Meantime his golden face around
He bares to all the garden ground,
And sheds a warm and glittering look
Among the ivy's inmost nook.

Above the hills, along the blue,
Round the bright air with footing true,
To please the child, to paint the rose,
The gardener of the World, he goes.

V

THE DUMB SOLDIER

WHEN the grass was closely mown,
Walking on the lawn alone,
In the turf a hole I found
And hid a soldier underground.

Spring and daisies came apace ;
Grasses hide my hiding-place ;
Grasses run like a green sea
O'er the lawn up to my knee.

Under grass alone he lies,
Looking up with leaden eyes,
Scarlet coat and pointed gun,
To the stars and to the sun.

When the grass is ripe like grain,
When the scythe is stoned again,
When the lawn is shaven clear,
Then my hole shall reappear.

I shall find him, never fear,
I shall find my grenadier ;
But, for all that's gone and come,
I shall find my soldier dumb.

He has lived, a little thing,
In the grassy woods of spring ;
Done, if he could tell me true,
Just as I should like to do.

He has seen the starry hours
And the springing of the flowers ;
And the fairy things that pass
In the forests of the grass.

In the silence he has heard
Talking bee and ladybird,
And the butterfly has flown
O'er him as he lay alone.

Not a word will he disclose,
Not a word of all he knows.
I must lay him on the shelf,
And make up the tale myself.

VI

AUTUMN FIRES

In the other gardens
    And all up the vale,
From the autumn bonfires
    See the smoke trail!

Pleasant summer over,
    And all the summer flowers,
The red fire blazes,
    The grey smoke towers.

Sing a song of seasons!
    Something bright in all!
Flowers in the summer,
    Fires in the fall!

VII

THE GARDENER

The gardener does not love to talk,
He makes me keep the gravel walk;
And when he puts his tools away,
He locks the door and takes the key

Away behind the currant row
Where, no one else but cook may go,
Far in the plots, I see him dig,
Old and serious, brown and big.

He digs the flowers, green, red, and blue,
Nor wishes to be spoken to.
He digs the flowers and cuts the hay,
And never seems to want to play.

Silly gardener! summer goes,
And winter comes with pinching toes,
When in the garden bare and brown
You must lay your barrow down.

Well now, and while the summer stays,
To profit by these garden days,
O how much wiser you would be
To play at Indian wars with me!

VIII

HISTORICAL ASSOCIATIONS

DEAR Uncle Jim, this garden ground,
That now you smoke your pipe around,
Has seen immortal actions done
And valiant battles lost and won.

Here we had best on tip-toe tread,
While I for safety march ahead,
For this is that enchanted ground
Where all who loiter slumber sound.

Here is the sea, here is the sand,
Here is simple Shepherd's Land,
Here are the fairy hollyhocks,
And there are Ali Baba's rocks.

But yonder, see! apart and high,
Frozen Siberia lies; where I,
With Robert Bruce and William Tell,
Was bound by an enchanter's spell.

There, then, a while in chains we lay,
In wintry dungeons, far from day;
But ris'n at length, with might and main,
Our iron fetters burst in twain.

Then all the horns were blown in town;
And, to the ramparts clanging down,
All the giants leaped to horse
And charged behind us through the gorse.

On we rode, the others and I,
Over the mountains blue, and by
The Silver River, the sounding sea,
And the robber woods of Tartary.

A thousand miles we galloped fast,
And down the witches' lane we passed,
And rode amain, with brandished sword,
Up to the middle, through the ford.

Last we drew rein—a weary three—
Upon the lawn, in time for tea,
And from our steeds alighted down
Before the gates of Babylon.

ENVOYS

I

TO WILLIE AND HENRIETTA

If two may read aright
These rhymes of old delight
And house and garden play,
You two, my cousins, and you only, may.

You in a garden green
With me were king and queen,
Were hunter, soldier, tar,
And all the thousand things that children are.

Now in the elders' seat
We rest with quiet feet,
And from the window-bay
We watch the children, our successors, play.

"Time was," the golden head
Irrevocably said;
But time which none can bind,
While flowing fast away, leaves love behind.

II

TO MY MOTHER

You too, my mother, read my rhymes
For love of unforgotten times,
And you may chance to hear once more
The little feet along the floor.

III
TO AUNTIE

Chief of our aunts—not only I,
But all your dozen of nurslings cry—
What did the other children do?
And what were childhood, wanting you?

IV
TO MINNIE

THE red room with the giant bed
Where none but elders laid their head;
The little room where you and I
Did for a while together lie,
And, simple suitor, I your hand
In decent marriage did demand;
The great day-nursery, best of all,
With pictures pasted on the wall
And leaves upon the blind—
A pleasant room wherein to wake
And hear the leafy garden shake
And rustle in the wind—
And pleasant there to lie in bed
And see the pictures overhead—
The wars about Sebastopol,
The grinning guns along the wall,
The daring escalade,
The plunging ships, the bleating sheep,
The happy children ankle-deep,
And laughing as they wade:

All these are vanished clean away,
And the old manse is changed to-day;
It wears an altered face
And shields a stranger race.

The river, on from mill to mill,
Flows past our childhood's garden still ;
But ah ! we children never more
Shall watch it from the water-door !
Below the yew—it still is there—
Our phantom voices haunt the air
As we were still at play,
And I can hear them call and say :
" *How far is it to Babylon?* "

Ah, far enough, my dear,
Far, far enough from here—
Yet you have farther gone !
" *Can I get there by candlelight?* "
So goes the old refrain.
I do not know—perchance you might—
But only, children, hear it right,
Ah, never to return again !
The eternal dawn, beyond a doubt,
Shall break on hill and plain,
And put all stars and candles out
Ere we be young again.

To you in distant India, these
I send across the seas,
Nor count it far across.
For which of us forgets
The Indian cabinets,
The bones of antelope, the wings of albatross,
The pied and painted birds and beans,
The junks and bangles, beads and screens,
The gods and sacred bells,
And the loud-humming, twisted shells ?
The level of the parlour floor
Was honest, homely, Scottish shore ;
But when we climbed upon a chair,
Behold the gorgeous East was there !
Be this a fable ; and behold
Me in the parlour as of old.

E

And Minnie just above me set
In the quaint Indian cabinet !
Smiling and kind, you grace a shelf
Too high for me to reach myself.
Reach down a hand, my dear, and take
These rhymes for old acquaintance' sake !

V

TO MY NAME-CHILD

I

SOME day soon this rhyming volume, if you learn with
    proper speed,
Little Louis Sanchez, will be given you to read.
Then shall you discover, that your name was printed
    down
By the English printers, long before, in London town.

In the great and busy city where the East and West are
    met,
All the little letters did the English printer set ;
While you thought of nothing, and were still too young
    to play,
Foreign people thought of you in places far away.

Ay, and while you slept, a baby, over all the English lands
Other little children took the volume in their hands ;
Other children questioned, in their homes across the seas :
Who was little Louis, won't you tell us, mother, please ?

2

Now that you have spelt your lesson, lay it down and go
    and play,
Seeking shells and seaweed on the sands of Monterey,
Watching all the mighty whalebones, lying buried by the
    breeze,
Tiny sandy-pipers, and the huge Pacific seas.

And remember in your playing, as the sea-fog rolls to you,
Long ere you could read it, how I told you what to do ;
And that while you thought of no one, nearly half the world
    away
Some one thought of Louis on the beach of Monterey !

VI

TO ANY READER

WHETHER upon the garden seat
You lounge with your uplifted feet
Under the May's whole Heaven of blue ;
Or whether on the sofa you,
No grown up person being by,
Do some soft corner occupy :
Take you this volume in your hands
And enter into other lands,
For lo ! (as children feign) suppose
You, hunting in the garden rows,
Or in the lumbered attic, or
The cellar—a nail-studded door
And dark, descending stairway found
That led to kingdoms underground :
There standing, you should hear with ease
Strange birds a-singing, or the trees
Swing in big robber woods, or bells
On many fairy citadels :
There passing through (a step or so
Neither mamma nor nurse need know !)
From your nice nurseries you would pass
Like Alice through the Looking-Glass
Or Gerda following Little Ray,
To wondrous countries far away.
Well, and just this volume can
Transport each little maid or man,
Presto, from where they live away
Where other children used to play.

As from the house your mother sees
You playing round the garden trees,
So you may see, if you but look
Through the windows of this book,
Another child, far, far away
And in another garden, play.
But do not think you can at all,
By knocking on the window, call
That child to hear you. He intent
Is still on his play-business bent.
He does not hear, he will not look,
Nor yet be lured out of this book.
For long ago, the truth to say,
He has grown up and gone away ;
And it is but a child of air
That lingers in the garden there.

UNDERWOODS

Of all my verse, like not a single line,
But like my title, for it is not mine.
That title from a better man I stole:
Ah, how much better, had I stol'n the whole!

The first collected edition of *Underwoods* (Books I and II) was published in 1887.

Songs of Travel were forwarded in proof to Sidney Colvin with a letter, dated May 18, 1894, in which the author said, "I am sending you a lot of verses, which had best, I think, be called *Underwoods*, Book III, but in what order are they to go?" Stevenson had tried them in several different orders and under several different titles, as *Songs and Notes of Travel, Vailima, Posthumous Poems,* etc., finally leaving the naming and arrangement to Mr. Colvin. They were published for the first time in the Edinburgh Edition.

PREFATORY NOTE

PREFATORY NOTE

By Mrs. R. L. Stevenson

VERY few of my husband's poems were conceived with any other purpose than the entertainment of the moment. *The Scotsman's Return from Abroad* was written to amuse his father when we were stopping with the family in Strathpeffar, a dreary " hydropathic " in the Highlands. Seven years after, in August, 1887, we were summoned by telegram to Edinburgh, where my father-in-law was fighting death inch by inch. His memory gone, his reason shattered, nothing remained but his determined will. It was a terrible figure we found sitting grimly in the drawing-room of the house at Heriot Row ; for it was not until an hour or two before his death, on the evening of our arrival, that he could be persuaded to lie upon his bed, and then only after a narcotic had been administered.

During the gloomy days that followed, my husband, who occupied the rooms that had been set apart for him in his boyhood, with the many evidences of his father's affection surrounding him on every side,—the books on the shelves, the childish toys still sacredly cherished,— found that he must turn his thoughts into other channels, or he would be unable to fulfil the duties that now devolved upon him. He resolutely sat himself at his desk and wrote *The Ballad of Ticonderoga*, the theme of which had already been discussed with his father before that fine intellect had become obscured by the clouds that settled round his last days.

The verses entitled *A Portrait*, so unlike anything else my husband ever wrote, do not explain themselves, and must have puzzled many of his readers. He had just finished, with wondering disgust, a book of poems in the most musical English, but excessively morbid and unpleasant in sentiment. His criticisms were generally sympathetic and kind; but this " battener upon garbage " with his " air of saying grace " was more than my husband could endure, and in the first heat of his indignation he wrote *A Portrait*.

It is said that when Mr. Kipling is heard humming a tune he is supposed to be composing a poem to fit the music. I think my husband must have used something of the same method, for in his library I found, among others, these verses written out to airs that had pleased him:

THE STORMY EVENING

Air after Oldfield

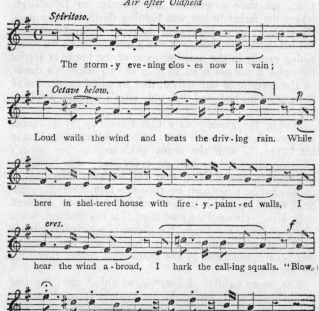

The storm-y eve-ning clos-es now in vain;

Loud wails the wind and beats the driv-ing rain. While

here in shel-tered house with fire-y-paint-ed walls, I

hear the wind a-broad, I hark the call-ing squalls. "Blow,

blow," I cry, "you burst your cheeks in vain!

p Grazioso.

Blow, blow," I cry, "my love is home a-gain! Blow,

blow," I cry, "my love is home a-gain!"

"WE HAVE LIVED AND LOVED"

Air after Diabelli—op. 168, No. 1

Andante expressivo.

Ber-ried brake and reed-y is-land, Heav'n be-

-low and on-ly heav'n a-bove, Thro' the skies' in-vert-ed

im-age Soft-ly swam the boat that

bore our love. Dear were your eyes as the

day; Bright ran the stream, bright hung the sky a-bove. Days of

A-pril, airs of E-den; How the glo-ry died thro'

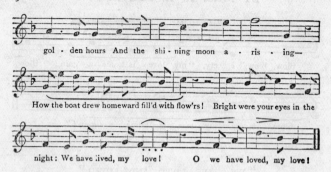

gol - den hours And the shi - ning moon a - ris - ing—

How the boat drew homeward fill'd with flow'rs!   Bright were your eyes in the

night: We have lived, my   love!   O   we have loved, my love!

The writing of *Over the Sea to Skye* grew out of a visit from one of the last of the old school of Scots gentlewomen, Miss Ferrier, a granddaughter of Professor Wilson (Christopher North). Her singing was a great delight to my husband, who would beg for song after song, especially the Jacobite airs, which had always to be repeated several times. The words to one of these seemed unworthy, so he made a new set of verses more in harmony with the plaintive tune:

OVER THE SEA TO SKYE

Gaelic Air

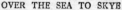

Animato.

Sing me a song of a lad that is gone,

Say, could that lad be I?   Mer - ry of soul, he

FINE.

sailed on a day   O - ver the sea to Skye.

Mull was a-stern, Rum on the port,

Eigg on the star-board bow; Glo-ry of youth

D.C.

glowed in his soul: Where is that glo-ry now?

The *Spae Wife* may have been due to unconscious memory. In the Scotland of my husband's childhood, nurses sometimes crooned to their charges ancient airs whose origin is forgotten, and whose words were long ago lost. A Scotsman, Mr. George St. J. Bremner, of San Francisco, has kindly written out one that perfectly corresponds with the peculiar movement of the poem. He says: " This melody, I firmly believe, must have been running through Mr. Stevenson's head when he wrote the *Spae Wife*. If ever words and music were especially adapted to each other, certainly this melody and the song fit each other like hand and glove. The upward cadence of the first three lines, suiting so exactly with the interrogative character of the words, and the coarse downward cadence of the last, suiting so exactly with the noncommittal answer of the ' Spae Wife,' leave no room for doubt that a reminiscence of one of ' Cummy's' lilts was haunting him at the time."

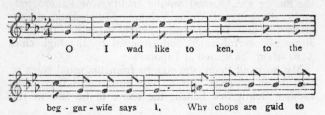

O I wad like to ken, to the

beg-gar-wife says I, Why chops are guid to

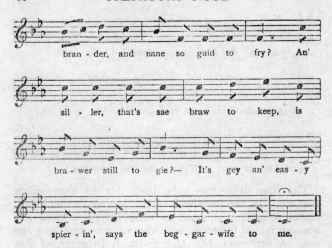

bran - der, and nane so guid to fry? An'

sil - ler, that's sae braw to keep, is

bra - wer still to gie?— It's gey an' eas - y

spier - in', says the beg - gar - wife to me.

An itinerary of my husband's wanderings might almost be drawn from his collected poems. *The Song of Rahéro* was first inspired by the conversation of the Princess Moe in Tautira, a village lying on the Tiarapu peninsula of Tahiti. Here we lived for several months, the guests of the princess and the chief Ori, with whom my husband "made brothers" in the island fashion. Although Moe was then grandmother to several tall girls, she was still beautiful, with much of the grace and charm of youth. It happened, while we were in Tautira, there was some legal question to be settled concerning lands, belonging to the princess, that lay in the country of Tiarapu. In discussing the matter she touched on the tradition of Rahéro, jestingly calling herself Ahupu Vehine. My husband, deeply interested, drew from her all she could tell him of the story, afterwards corroborated and enriched by the high chief Tati, whom we visited at Papora.

My husband found the change from his usual work so restful and pleasant that he was encouraged to attempt another South Sea ballad, the scene to be laid in the

Marquesas. · This ballad, begun in Tautira, was finished on board the yacht *Casco*, between Tahiti and Hawaii, amid every possible discomfort. Our provisions (all we could get in Tahiti) were scant and bad ; we carried a hurricane barometer all the way, and were constantly beset by squalls and baffling winds. For two days we lay becalmed off Oahu, the tantalising sight of land before our eyes. During the time we spent in Tautira we lived almost entirely on native food ; this, followed by thirty days of decayed beef and stale biscuits, reduced us to a state of semi-starvation. I shall never forget our first dinner on shore at Honolulu, with its roasts and potatoes and celery, and that

> "Rose among roots, the maiden fair,
> Wine scented and poetic soul
> Of the capacious salad bowl."

F. V. DE G. S.

DEDICATION

There are men and classes of men that stand above the common herd : the soldier, the sailor, and the shepherd not unfrequently ; the artist rarely ; rarelier still, the clergyman ; the physician almost as a rule. He is the flower (such as it is) of our civilisation ; and when that stage of man is done with, and only remembered to be marvelled at in history, he will be thought to have shared as little as any in the defects of the period, and most notably exhibited the virtues of the race. Generosity he has, such as is possible to those who practise an art, never to those who drive a trade ; discretion, tested by a hundred secrets ; tact, tried in a thousand embarrassments ; and, what are more important, Heraclean cheerfulness and courage. So it is that he brings air and cheer into the sick-room, and often enough, though not so often as he wishes, brings healing.

Gratitude is but a lame sentiment ; thanks, when they are expressed, are often more embarrassing than welcome ; and yet I must set forth mine to a few out of many doctors who have brought me comfort and help : to Dr. Willey of San Francisco, whose kindness to a stranger it must be as grateful to him, as it is touching to me, to remember ; to Dr. Karl Ruedi of Davos, the good genius of the English in his frosty mountains ; to Dr. Herbert of Paris, whom I knew only for a week, and to Dr. Caissot of Montpellier, whom I knew only for ten days, and who have yet written their names deeply in my memory ; to Dr. Brandt of Royat ; to Dr. Wakefield of Nice ; to Dr. Chepmell, whose visits make it a pleasure to be ill ; to Dr. Horace Dobell, so wise in counsel ; to Sir Andrew Clark, so unwearied in kindness ; and to that wise youth, my uncle, Dr. Balfour.

I forget as many as I remember; and I ask both to pardon me, these for silence, those for inadequate speech. But one

name I have kept on purpose to the last, because it is a house-
hold word with me, and because if I had not received favours
from so many hands and in so many quarters of the world,
it should have stood upon this page alone : that of my friend
Thomas Bodley Scott of Bournemouth. Will he accept this,
although shared among so many, for a dedication to himself?
and when next my ill-fortune (which has thus its pleasant
side) brings him hurrying to me when he would fain sit
down to meat or lie down to rest, will he care to remember
that he takes this trouble for one who is not fool enough to be
ungrateful?

R. L. S.

Skerryvore,
Bournemouth.

BOOK I

UNDERWOODS

On every hand the roads begin,

UNDERWOODS

I

ENVOY

Go, little book, and wish to all
Flowers in the garden, meat in the hall,
A bin of wine, a spice of wit,
A house with lawns enclosing it,
A living river by the door,
A nightingale in the sycamore !

II

A SONG OF THE ROAD

THE gauger walked with willing foot,
And aye the gauger played the flute ;
And what should Master Gauger play
But *Over the hills and far away?*

Whene'er I buckle on my pack
And foot it gaily in the track,
A pleasant gauger, long since dead,
I hear you fluting on ahead.

You go with me the self-same way—
The self-same air for me you play ;
For I do think and so do you
It is the tune to travel to.

For who would gravely set his face
To go to this or t'other place ?
There's nothing under Heav'n so blue
That's fairly worth the travelling to.

On every hand the roads begin,
And people walk with zeal therein :
But wheresoe'er the highways tend,
Be sure there's nothing at the end.

Then follow you, wherever hie
The travelling mountains of the sky,
Or let the streams in civil mode
Direct your choice upon a road ;

For one and all, or high or low,
Will lead you where you wish to go ;
And one and all go night and day
Over the hills and far away !

FOREST OF MONTARGIS, 1878.

III

THE CANOE SPEAKS

ON the great streams the ships may go
About men's business to and fro,
But I, the egg-shell pinnace, sleep
On crystal waters ankle-deep :
I, whose diminutive design,
Of sweeter cedar, pithier pine,
Is fashioned on so frail a mould,
A hand may launch, a hand withhold :
I, rather, with the leaping trout
Wind, among lilies, in and out ;
I, the unnamed, inviolate,
Green, rustic rivers navigate ;
My dipping paddle scarcely shakes
The berry in the bramble-brakes ;
Still forth on my green way I wend
Beside the cottage garden-end ;
And by the nested angler fare,
And take the lovers unaware.

By willow wood and water-wheel
Speedily fleets my touching keel ;
By all retired and shady spots
Where prosper dim forget-me-nots ;
By meadows where at afternoon
The growing maidens troop in June
To loose their girdles on the grass.
Ah ! speedier than before the glass
The backward toilet goes ; and swift
As swallows quiver, robe and shift
And the rough country stockings lie
Around each young divinity.
When, following the recondite brook,
Sudden upon this scene I look,
And light with unfamiliar face
On chaste Diana's bathing-place,
Loud ring the hills about and all
The shallows are abandoned. . . .

IV

IT is the season now to go
About the country high and low,
Among the lilacs hand in hand,
And two by two in fairyland.

The brooding boy, the sighing maid,
Wholly fain and half afraid,
Now meet along the hazel'd brook
To pass and linger, pause and look.

A year ago, and blithely paired,
Their rough-and-tumble play they shared ;
They kissed and quarrelled, laughed and cried,
A year ago at Eastertide.

With bursting heart, with fiery face,
She strove against him in the race ;
He unabashed her garter saw,
That now would touch her skirts with awe.

Now by the stile ablaze she stops,
And his demurer eyes he drops;
Now they exchanged averted sighs
Or stand and marry silent eyes.

And he to her a hero is
And sweeter she than primroses;
Their common silence dearer far
Than nightingale or mavis are.

Now when they sever wedded hands,
Joy trembles in their bosom-strands,
And lovely laughter leaps and falls
Upon their lips in madrigals.

V

THE HOUSE BEAUTIFUL

A naked house, a naked moor,
A shivering pool before the door,
A garden bare of flowers and fruit,
And poplars at the garden foot:
Such is the place that I live in,
Bleak without and bare within.

Yet shall your ragged moor receive
The incomparable pomp of eve,
And the cold glories of the dawn
Behind your shivering trees be drawn;
And when the wind from place to place
Doth the unmoored cloud-galleons chase,
Your garden gloom and gleam again,
With leaping sun, with glancing rain.
Here shall the wizard moon ascend
The heavens, in the crimson end
Of day's declining splendour; here
The army of the stars appear.
The neighbour hollows, dry or wet,
Spring shall with tender flowers beset;

And oft the morning muser see
Larks rising from the broomy lea,
And every fairy wheel and thread
Of cobweb dew-bediamonded.
When daisies go, shall winter-time
Silver the simple grass with rime ;
Autumnal frosts enchant the pool
And make the cart-ruts beautiful ;
And when snow-bright the moor expands,
How shall your children clap their hands !

To make this earth, our hermitage,
A cheerful and a changeful page,
God's bright and intricate device
Of days and seasons doth suffice.

VI

A VISIT FROM THE SEA

FAR from the loud sea beaches
    Where he goes fishing and crying,
Here in the inland garden
    Why is the sea-gull flying ?

Here are no fish to dive for ;
    Here is the corn and lea ;
Here are the green trees rustling.
    Hie away home to sea !

Fresh is the river water
    And quiet among the rushes ;
This is no home for the sea-gull,
    But for the rooks and thrushes.

Pity the bird that has wandered !
    Pity the sailor ashore !
Hurry him home to the ocean,
    Let him come here no more !

High on the sea-cliff ledges
    The white gulls are trooping and crying,
Here among rooks and roses,
    Why is the sea-gull flying?

VII

TO A GARDENER

FRIEND, in my mountain-side demesne,
My plain-beholding, rosy, green
And linnet-haunted garden-ground,
Let still the esculents abound.
Let first the onion flourish there,
Rose among roots, the maiden-fair,
Wine-scented and poetic soul
Of the capacious salad-bowl.
Let thyme the mountaineer (to dress
The tinier birds) and wading cress,
The lover of the shallow brook,
From all my plots and borders look.
Nor crisp and ruddy radish, nor
Pease-cods for the child's pinafore
Be lacking; nor of salad clan
The last and least that ever ran
About great Nature's garden-beds.
Nor thence be missed the speary heads
Of artichoke; nor thence the bean
That gathered innocent and green
Outsavours the belauded pea.

These tend, I prithee; and for me,
Thy most long-suffering master, bring
In April, when the linnets sing
And the days lengthen more and more,
At sundown to the garden door.
And I, being provided thus,
Shall, with superb asparagus,
A book, a taper, and a cup
Of country wine, divinely sup.

LA SOLITUDE, HYÈRES.

VIII

TO MINNIE

(WITH A HAND-GLASS)

A PICTURE-FRAME for you to fill,
　A paltry setting for your face,
A thing that has no worth until
　You lend it something of your grace,

I send (unhappy I that sing
　Laid by a while upon the shelf)
Because I would not send a thing
　Less charming than you are yourself.

And happier than I, alas!
　(Dumb thing, I envy its delight)
'T will wish you well, the looking-glass,
　And look you in the face to-night.
1869.

IX

TO K. DE M.

A LOVER of the moorland bare
And honest country winds you were;
The silver-skimming rain you took;
And loved the floodings of the brook,
Dew, frost and mountains, fire and seas,
Tumultuary silences,
Winds that in darkness fifed a tune,
And the high-riding, virgin moon.

And as the berry, pale and sharp,
Springs on some ditch's counterscarp
In our ungenial, native north—
You put your frosted wildings forth,
And on the heath, afar from man,
A strong and bitter virgin ran.

The berry ripened keeps the rude
And racy flavour of the wood.
And you that loved the empty plain
All redolent of wind and rain,
Around you still the curlew sings—
The freshness of the weather clings—
The maiden jewels of the rain
Sit in your dabbled locks again.

X

TO N. V. DE G. S.

THE unfathomable sea, and time, and tears,
The deeds of heroes and the crimes of kings,
Dispart us ; and the river of events
Has, for an age of years, to east and west
More widely borne our cradles. Thou to me
Art foreign, as when seamen at the dawn
Descry a land far off and know not which.
So I approach uncertain ; so I cruise
Round thy mysterious islet, and behold
Surf and great mountains and loud river-bars,
And from the shore hear inland voices call.
Strange is the seaman's heart ; he hopes, he fears ;
Draws closer and sweeps wider from that coast ;
Last, his rent sail refits, and to the deep
His shattered prow uncomforted puts back.
Yet as he goes he ponders at the helm
Of that bright island ; where he feared to touch,
His spirit re-adventures ; and for years,
Where by his wife he slumbers safe at home,
Thoughts of that land revisit him ; he sees
The eternal mountains beckon, and awakes
Yearning for that far home that might have been.

XI

TO WILL H. LOW

YOUTH now flees on feathered foot.
Faint and fainter sounds the flute,

Rarer songs of gods ; and still
Somewhere on the sunny hill,
Or along the winding stream,
Through the willows flits a dream ;
Flits, but shows a smiling face,
Flees, but with so quaint a grace,
None can choose to stay at home,
All must follow, all must roam.

This is unborn beauty : she
Now in air floats high and free,
Takes the sun and breaks the blue ;—
Late with stooping pinion flew
Raking hedgerow trees, and wet
Her wing in silver streams, and set
Shining foot on temple roof :
Now again she flies aloof,
Coasting mountain clouds and kiss't
By the evening's amethyst.

In wet wood and miry lane,
Still we pant and pound in vain ;
Still with leaden foot we chase
Waning pinion, fainting face ;
Still with grey hair we stumble on,
Till, behold, the vision gone !
Where hath fleeting beauty led ?
To the doorway of the dead.
Life is over, life was gay :
We have come the primrose way.

XII

TO MRS. WILL H. LOW

EVEN in the bluest noonday of July
There could not run the smallest breath of wind
But all the quarter sounded like a wood ;
And in the chequered silence, and above

The hum of city cabs that sought the Bois,
Suburban ashes shivered into song.
A patter and a chatter and a chirp
And a long dying hiss—it was as though
Starched old brocaded dames through all the house
Had trailed a strident skirt, or the whole sky
Even in a wink had over-brimmed in rain.
Hark, in these shady parlours, how it talks
Of the near autumn, how the smitten ash
Trembles and augurs floods ! O not too long
In these inconstant latitudes delay,
O not too late from the unbeloved north
Trim your escape ! For soon shall this low roof
Resound indeed with rain, soon shall your eyes
Search the foul garden, search the darkened rooms,
Nor find one jewel but the blazing log.

12 RUE VERNIER, PARIS.

XIII

TO H. F. BROWN

(WRITTEN DURING A DANGEROUS SICKNESS)

I SIT and wait a pair of oars
On cis-Elysian river-shores.
Where the immortal dead have sate,
'Tis mine to sit and meditate ;
To re-ascend life's rivulet,
Without remorse, without regret ;
And sing my *Alma Genetrix*
Among the willows of the Styx.

And lo, as my serener soul
Did these unhappy shores patrol,
And wait with an attentive ear
The coming of the gondolier,
Your fire-surviving roll I took,
Your spirited and happy book ; [1]

[1] *Life on the Lagoons*, by H. F. Brown, originally burned in the fire at Messrs. Kegan Paul, Trench and Co.'s.

Whereon, despite my frowning fate,
It did my soul so recreate
That all my fancies fled away
On a Venetian holiday.

Now, thanks to your triumphant care,
Your pages clear as April air,
The sails, the bells, the birds, I know,
And the far-off Friulan snow ;
The land and sea, the sun and shade,
And the blue even lamp-inlaid.
For this, for these, for all, O friend,
For your whole book from end to end—
For Paron Piero's mutton-ham—
I your defaulting debtor am.

Perchance, reviving, yet may I
To your sea-paven city hie,
And in a *felze*, some day yet
Light at your pipe my cigarette.

XIV

TO ANDREW LANG

DEAR Andrew, with the brindled hair,
Who glory to have thrown in air,
High over arm, the trembling reed,
By Ale and Kail, by Till and Tweed :
An equal craft of hand you show
The pen to guide, the fly to throw :
I count you happy-starred ; for God,
When He with inkpot and with rod
Endowed you, bade your fortune lead
For ever by the crooks of Tweed,
For ever by the woods of song
And lands that to the Muse belong ;
Or if in peopled streets, or in
The abhorred pedantic sanhedrin,

It should be yours to wander, still
Airs of the morn, airs of the hill,
The plovery Forest and the seas
That break about the Hebrides,
Should follow over field and plain
And find you at the window-pane ;
And you again see hill and peel,
And the bright springs gush at your heel.
So went the fiat forth, and so
Garrulous like a brook you go,
With sound of happy mirth and sheen
Of daylight—whether by the green
You fare that moment, or the grey ;
Whether you dwell in March or May ;
Or whether treat of reels and rods
Or of the old unhappy gods :
Still like a brook your page has shone,
And your ink sings of Helicon.

XV

ET TU IN ARCADIA VIXISTI

(TO R. A. M. S.[1])

IN ancient tales, O friend, thy spirit dwelt ;
There, from of old, thy childhood passed ; and there
High expectation, high delights and deeds,
Thy fluttering heart with hope and terror moved.
And thou hast heard of yore the Blatant Beast,
And Roland's horn, and that war-scattering shout
Of all-unarmed Achilles, ægis-crowned.
And perilous lands thou sawest, sounding shores
And seas and forests drear, island and dale
And mountain dark. For thou with Tristram rod'st
Or Bedevere, in farthest Lyonesse.
Thou hadst a booth in Samarcand, whereat
Side-looking Magians trafficked ; thence, by night,
An Afreet snatched thee, and with wings upbore

---

[1] Stevenson's cousin, Robert A. M. Stevenson.

Beyond the Aral mount ; or, hoping gain,
Thou, with a jar of money, didst embark
For Balsorah by sea.   But chiefly thou
In that clear air took'st life ; in Arcady
The haunted, land of song ; and by the wells
Where most the gods frequent.   There Chiron old,
In the Pelethronian antre, taught thee lore ;
The planets he taught, and by the shining stars
In forests dim to steer.   There hast thou seen
Immortal Pan dance secret in a glade,
And, dancing, roll his eyes ; these, where they fell,
Shed glee, and through the congregated oaks
A flying horror winged ; while all the earth
To the god's pregnant footing thrilled within.
Or whiles, beside the sobbing stream, he breathed
In his clutched pipe unformed and wizard strains,
Divine yet brutal ; which the forest heard,
And thou, with awe ; and far upon the plain
The unthinking ploughman started and gave ear.
Now things there are that, upon him who sees,
A strong vocation lay ; and strains there are
That whoso hears shall hear for evermore.
For evermore thou hear'st immortal Pan
And those melodious godheads, ever young
And ever quiring, on the mountains old.
What was this earth, child of the gods, to thee ?
Forth from thy dreamland thou, a dreamer, cam'st,
And in thine ears the olden music rang,
And in thy mind the doings of the dead,
And those heroic ages long forgot.
To a so fallen earth, alas ! too late,
Alas ! in evil days, thy steps return,
To list at noon for nightingales, to grow
A dweller on the beach till Argo come
That came long since, a lingerer by the pool
Where that desirèd angel bathes no more.

As when the Indian to Dakota comes,
Or farthest Idaho, and where he dwelt.

He with his clan, a humming city finds;
Thereon a while, amazed, he stares, and then
To right and leftward, like a questing dog,
Seeks first the ancestral altars, then the hearth
Long cold with rains, and where old terror lodged,
And where the dead. So thee undying Hope,
With all her pack, hunts screaming through the years:
Here, there, thou fleeëst; but nor here nor there
The pleasant gods abide, the glory dwells.
That, that was not Apollo, not the god.
This was not Venus, though she Venus seemed
A moment. And though fair yon river move,
She, all the way, from disenchanted fount
To seas unhallowed runs; the gods forsook
Long since her trembling rushes; from her plains
Disconsolate, long since adventure fled;
And now although the inviting river flows,
And every poplared cape, and every bend
Or willowy islet, win upon thy soul
And to thy hopeful shallop whisper speed;
Yet hope not thou at all; hope is no more;
And O, long since the golden groves are dead,
The faëry cities vanished from the land!

XVI

TO W. E. HENLEY

THE year runs through her phases; rain and sun,
Spring-time and summer pass; winter succeeds;
But one pale season rules the house of death.
Cold falls the imprisoned daylight; fell disease
By each lean pallet squats, and pain and sleep
Toss gaping on the pillows.
                                        But O thou!
Uprise and take thy pipe. Bid music flow,
Strains by good thoughts attended, like the spring
The swallows follow over land and sea.
Pain sleeps at once; at once, with open eyes.

Dozing despair awakes. The shepherd sees
His flock come bleating home ; the seaman hears
Once more the cordage rattle. Airs of home !
Youth, love, and roses blossom ; the gaunt ward
Dislimns and disappears, and, opening out,
Shows brooks and forests, and the blue beyond
Of mountains.

           Small the pipe : but O ! do thou,
Peak-faced and suffering piper, blow therein
The dirge of heroes dead ; and to these sick,
These dying, sound the triumph over death.
Behold ! each greatly breathes ; each tastes a joy
Unknown before, in dying ; for each knows
A hero dies with him—though unfulfilled,
Yet conquering truly—and not dies in vain.

So is pain cheered, death comforted ; the house
Of sorrow smiles to listen. Once again—
O thou, Orpheus and Heracles, the bard
And the deliverer, touch the stops again !

XVII

HENRY JAMES

WHO comes to-night ? We ope the doors in vain.
Who comes ? My bursting walls, can you contain
The presences that now together throng
Your narrow entry, as with flowers and song,
As with the air of life, the breath of talk ?
Lo, how these fair immaculate women walk
Behind their jocund maker ; and we see
Slighted *De Mauves*, and that far different she,
Gressie, the trivial sphynx ; and to our feast
Daisy and *Barb* and *Chancellor* (she not least !)
With all their silken, all their airy kin,
Do like unbidden angels enter in.
But he, attended by these shining names,
Comes (best of all) himself—our welcome James.

G

XVIII

THE MIRROR SPEAKS

WHERE the bells peal far at sea
Cunning fingers fashioned me.
There on palace walls I hung
While that Consuelo sung ;
But I heard, though I listened well,
Never a note, never a trill,
Never a beat of the chiming bell.
There I hung and looked, and there
In my grey face, faces fair
Shone from under shining hair.
Well I saw the poising head,
But the lips moved and nothing said ;
And when lights were in the hall,
Silent moved the dancers all.

So a while I glowed, and then
Fell on dusty days and men ;
Long I slumbered packed in straw,
Long I none but dealers saw ;
Till before my silent eye
One that sees came passing by.

Now with an outlandish grace,
To the sparkling fire I face
In the blue room at Skerryvore ;
Where I wait until the door
Open, and the Prince of Men,
Henry James, shall come again.

XIX

KATHARINE

WE see you as we see a face
That trembles in a forest place
Upon the mirror of a pool
For ever quiet, clear and cool ;

And in the wayward glass, appears
To hover between smiles and tears,
Elfin and human, airy and true,
And backed by the reflected blue.

XX

TO F. J. S.

I READ, dear friend, in your dear face
Your life's tale told with perfect grace;
The river of your life I trace
Up the sun-chequered, devious bed
To the far-distant fountain-head.

Not one quick beat of your warm heart,
Nor thought that came to you apart,
Pleasure nor pity, love nor pain
Nor sorrow, has gone by in vain;

But as some lone, wood-wandering child
Brings home with him at evening mild
The thorns and flowers of all the wild,
From your whole life, O fair and true
Your flowers and thorns you bring with you!

XXI

REQUIEM

UNDER the wide and starry sky,
Dig the grave and let me lie.
Glad did I live and gladly die,
    And I laid me down with a will.

This be the verse you grave for me:
Here he lies where he longed to be,
Home is the sailor, home from sea,
    And the hunter home from the hill.

HYÈRES, *May* 1884.

XXII

THE CELESTIAL SURGEON

If I have faltered more or less
In my great task of happiness;
If I have moved among my race
And shown no glorious morning face;
If beams from happy human eyes
Have moved me not; if morning skies,
Books, and my food, and summer rain
Knocked on my sullen heart in vain :—
Lord, Thy most pointed pleasure take
And stab my spirit broad awake;
Or, Lord, if too obdurate I,
Choose Thou, before that spirit die,
A piercing pain, a killing sin,
And to my dead heart run them in!

XXIII

OUR LADY OF THE SNOWS

Out of the sun, out of the blast,
Out of the world, alone I passed
Across the moor and through the wood
To where the monastery stood.
There neither lute nor breathing fife,
Nor rumour of the world of life,
Nor confidences low and dear,
Shall strike the meditative ear.
Aloof, unhelpful, and unkind,
The prisoners of the iron mind,
Where nothing speaks except the bell,
The unfraternal brothers dwell.

Poor passionate men, still clothed afresh
With agonising folds of flesh;
Whom the clear eyes solicit still
To some bold output of the will,

While fairy Fancy far before
And musing Memory-Hold-the-door
Now to heroic death invite
And now uncurtain fresh delight :
O, little boots it thus to dwell
On the remote unneighboured hill !

O to be up and doing, O
Unfearing and unshamed to go
In all the uproar and the press
About my human business !
My undissuaded heart I hear
Whisper courage in my ear.
With voiceless calls, the ancient earth
Summons me to a daily birth.
Thou, O my love, ye, O my friends—
The gist of life, the end of ends—
To laugh, to love, to live, to die,
Ye call me by the ear and eye !

Forth from the casemate, on the plain
Where honour has the world to gain,
Pour forth and bravely do your part,
O knights of the unshielded heart
Forth and for ever forward !—out
From prudent turret and redoubt,
And in the mellay charge amain,
To fall but yet to rise again !
Captive ? ah, still, to honour bright,
A captive soldier of the right !
Or free and fighting, good with ill ?
Unconquering but unconquered still !

And ye, O brethren, what if God,
When from Heav'n's top He spies abroad,
And sees on this tormented stage
The noble war of mankind rage :
What if His vivifying eye,
O monks, should pass your corner by ?

For still the Lord is Lord of might ;
In deeds, in deeds, He takes delight ;
The plough, the spear, the laden barks,
The field, the founded city, marks ;
He marks the smiler of the streets,
The singer upon garden seats ;
He sees the climber in the rocks ;
To Him, the shepherd folds his flocks.
For those He loves that underprop
With daily virtues Heaven's top,
And bear the falling sky with ease,
Unfrowning caryatides.
Those He approves that ply the trade,
That rock the child, that wed the maid,
That with weak virtues, weaker hands,
Sow gladness on the peopled lands,
And still with laughter, song and shout,
Spin the great wheel of earth about.

But ye ?—O ye who linger still
Here in your fortress on the hill,
With placid face, with tranquil breath,
The unsought volunteers of death,
Our cheerful General on high
With careless looks may pass you by.

XXIV

NOT yet, my soul, these friendly fields desert,
Where thou with grass, and rivers, and the breeze,
And the bright face of day, thy dalliance hadst ;
Where to thine ear first sang the enraptured birds ;
Where love and thou that lasting bargain made.
The ship rides trimmed, and from the eternal shore
Thou hearest airy voices ; but not yet
Depart, my soul, not yet a while depart.

Freedom is far, rest far. Thou art with life
Too closely woven, nerve with nerve entwined ;

Service still craving service, love for love,
Love for dear love, still suppliant with tears.
Alas, not yet thy human task is done !
A bond at birth is forged ; a debt doth lie
Immortal on mortality. It grows—
By vast rebound it grows, unceasing growth ;
Gift upon gift, alms upon alms, upreared,
From man, from God, from nature, till the soul
At that so huge indulgence stands amazed.

Leave not, my soul, the unfoughten field, nor leave
Thy debts dishonoured, nor thy place desert
Without due service rendered. For thy life,
Up, spirit, and defend that fort of clay,
Thy body, now beleaguered ; whether soon
Or late she fall ; whether to-day thy friends
Bewail thee dead, or, after years, a man
Grown old in honour and the friend of peace.
Contend, my soul, for moments and for hours ;
Each is with service pregnant ; each reclaimed
Is as a kingdom conquered, where to reign.

As when a captain rallies to the fight
His scattered legions, and beats ruin back,
He, on the field, encamps, well pleased in mind.
Yet surely him shall fortune overtake,
Him smite in turn, headlong his ensigns drive ;
And that dear land, now safe, to-morrow fall.
But he, unthinking, in the present good
Solely delights, and all the camps rejoice.

XXV

It is not yours, O mother, to complain,
    Not, mother, yours to weep,
Though nevermore your son again
    Shall to your bosom creep,
    Though nevermore again you watch your baby sleep.

Though in the greener paths of earth,
  Mother and child, no more
We wander ; and no more the birth
  Of me whom once you bore
Seems still the brave reward that once it seemed of yore ;

Though as all passes, day and night,
  The seasons and the years,
From you, O mother, this delight,
  This also disappears—
Some profit yet survives of all your pangs and tears

The child, the seed, the grain of corn,
  The acorn on the hill,
Each for some separate end is born
  In season fit, and still
Each must in strength arise to work the almighty will.

So from the hearth the children flee,
  By that almighty hand
Austerely led ; so one by sea
  Goes forth, and one by land ;
Nor aught of all man's sons escapes from that command.

So from the sally each obeys
  The unseen almighty nod ;
So till the ending all their ways
  Blindfolded loth have trod :
Nor knew their task at all, but were the tools of God.

And as the fervent smith of yore
  Beat out the glowing blade,
Nor wielded in the front of war
  The weapons that he made,
But in the tower at home still plied his ringing trade ;

So like a sword the son shall roam
  On nobler missions sent ;
And as the smith remained at home
  In peaceful turret pent,
So sits the while at home the mother well content.

XXVI

THE SICK CHILD

Child. O MOTHER, lay your hand on my brow !
O mother, mother, where am I now ?
Why is the room so gaunt and great ?
Why am I lying awake so late ?

Mother. Fear not at all : the night is still.
Nothing is here that means you ill—
Nothing but lamps the whole town through,
And never a child awake but you.

Child. Mother, mother, speak low in my ear,
Some of the things are so great and near,
Some are so small and far away.
I have a fear that I cannot say.
What have I done, and what do I fear,
And why are you crying, mother dear ?

Mother. Out in the city, sounds begin ;
Thank the kind God, the carts come in !
An hour or two more, and God is so kind,
The day shall be blue in the window-blind,
Then shall my child go sweetly asleep,
And dream of the birds and the hills of sheep.

XXVII

IN MEMORIAM F. A. S.

YET, O stricken heart, remember, O remember
How of human days he lived the better part.
April came to bloom and never dim December
Breathed its killing chills upon the head or heart.

Doomed to know not Winter, only Spring, a being
Trod the flowery April blithely for a while,
Took his fill of music, joy of thought and seeing,
Came and stayed and went, nor ever ceased to smile.

Came and stayed and went, and now when all is finished,
    You alone have crossed the melancholy stream,
Yours the pang, but his, O his, the undiminished
    Undecaying gladness, undeparted dream.

All that life contains of torture, toil, and treason,
    Shame, dishonour, death, to him were but a name.
Here, a boy, he dwelt through all the singing season,
    And ere the day of sorrow departed as he came.

DAVOS, 1881.

XXVIII

TO MY FATHER

PEACE and her huge invasion to these shores
Puts daily home ; innumerable sails
Dawn on the far horizon and draw near ;
Innumerable loves, uncounted hopes
To our wild coasts, not darkling now, approach :
Not now obscure, since thou and thine are there,
And bright on the lone isle, the foundered reef,
The long, resounding foreland, Pharos stands.

These are thy works, O father, these thy crown ;
Whether on high the air be pure, they shine
Along the yellowing sunset, and all night
Among the unnumbered stars of God they shine ;
Or whether fogs arise and far and wide
The low sea-level drown—each finds a tongue
And all night long the tolling bell resounds :
So shine, so toll, till night be overpast,
Till the stars vanish, till the sun return,
And in the haven rides the fleet secure.

In the first hour, the seaman in his skiff
Moves through the unmoving bay, to where the town
Its earliest smoke into the air upbreathes,
And the rough hazels climb along the beach.

To the tugg'd oar the distant echo speaks.
The ship lies resting, where by reef and roost
Thou and thy lights have led her like a child.

This hast thou done, and I—can I be base?
I must arise, O father, and to port
Some lost, complaining seaman pilot home.

XXIX

IN THE STATES

WITH half a heart I wander here,
　As from an age gone by
A brother—yet though young in years,
　An elder brother, I.

You speak another tongue than mine,
　Though both were English born.
I towards the night of time decline,
　You mount into the morn.

Youth shall grow great and strong and free,
　But age must still decay:
To-morrow for the States,—for me,
　England and Yesterday.

SAN FRANCISCO.

XXX

A PORTRAIT

I AM a kind of farthing dip,
　Unfriendly to the nose and eyes;
A blue-behinded ape, I skip
　Upon the trees of Paradise.

At mankind's feast, I take my place
　In solemn, sanctimonious state,
And have the air of saying grace
　While I defile the dinner-plate.

I am " the smiler with the knife,"
    The battener upon garbage, I—
Dear Heaven, with such a rancid life,
    Were it not better far to die ?

Yet still, about the human pale,
    I love to scamper, love to race,
To swing by my irreverent tail
    All over the most holy place ;

And when at length, some golden day,
    The unfailing sportsman, aiming at,
Shall bag, me—all the world shall say :
    Thank God, and there's an end of that !

XXXI

SING clearlier, Muse, or evermore be still,
Sing truer or no longer sing !
No more the voice of melancholy Jaques
To wake a weeping echo in the hill ;
But as the boy, the pirate of the spring,
From the green elm a living linnet takes,
One natural verse recapture—then be still.

XXXII

A CAMP[1]

THE bed was made, the room was fit,
By punctual eve the stars were lit ;
The air was still, the water ran,
No need was there for maid or man,
When we put up, my ass and I,
At God's green caravanserai.

[1] From *Travels with a Donkey.*

XXXIII

THE COUNTRY OF THE CAMISARDS [1]

WE travelled in the print of olden wars,
    Yet all the land was green,
    And love we found, and peace,
    Where fire and war had been.

They pass and smile, the children of the sword—
    No more the sword they wield;
    And O, how deep the corn
    Along the battle-field!

XXXIV

SKERRYVORE

FOR love of lovely words, and for the sake
Of those, my kinsmen and my countrymen,
Who early and late in the windy ocean toiled
To plant a star for seamen, where was then
The surfy haunt of seals and cormorants:
I, on the lintel of this cot, inscribe
The name of a strong tower.

XXXV

SKERRYVORE:

THE PARALLEL

HERE all is sunny, and when the truant gull
Skims the green level of the lawn, his wing
Dispetals roses; here the house is framed
Of kneaded brick and the plumed mountain pine,
Such clay as artists fashion and such wood
As the tree-climbing urchin breaks. But there
Eternal granite hewn from the living isle,

[1] From *Travels with a Donkey.*

And dowelled with brute iron, rears a tower
That, from its wet foundation to its crown
Of glittering glass, stands, in the sweep of winds,
Immovable, immortal, eminent.

XXXVI

My house, I say. But hark to the sunny doves
That make my roof the arena of their loves,
That gyre about the gable all day long
And fill the chimneys with their murmurous song;
Our house, they say; and *mine*, the cat declares,
And spreads his golden fleece upon the chairs;
And *mine* the dog, and rises stiff with wrath
If any alien foot profane the path.
So, too, the buck that trimmed my terraces,
Our whilome gardener, called the garden his;
Who now, deposed, surveys my plain abode
And his late kingdom, only from the road.

XXXVII

My body which my dungeon is,
And yet my parks and palaces :—
Which is so great that there I go
All the day long to and fro,
And when the night begins to fall
Throw down my bed and sleep, while all
The building hums with wakefulness—
Even as a child of savages
When evening takes her on her way,
(She having roamed a summer's day
Along the mountain-sides and scalp,)
Sleeps in an antre of that alp :—
    Which is so broad and high that there,
As in the topless fields of air,
My fancy soars like to a kite
And faints in the blue infinite :—

Which is so strong, my strongest throes
And the rough world's besieging blows
Not break it, and so weak withal,
Death ebbs and flows in its loose wall
As the green sea in fishers' nets,
And tops its topmost parapets :—
    Which is so wholly mine that I
Can wield its whole artillery,
And mine so little, that my soul
Dwells in perpetual control,
And I but think and speak and do
As my dead fathers move me to :—
    If this born body of my bones
The beggared soul so barely owns,
What money passed from hand to hand,
What creeping custom of the land,
What deed of author or assign,
Can make a house a thing of mine ?

XXXVIII

Say not of me that weakly I declined
The labours of my sires, and fled the sea,
The towers we founded and the lamps we lit,
To play at home with paper like a child.
But rather say : *In the afternoon of time*
A strenuous family dusted from its hands
The sand of granite, and beholding far
Along the sounding coast its pyramids
And tall memorials catch the dying sun,
Smiled well content, and to this childish task
Around the fire addressed its evening hours.

XXXIX

DEDICATORY POEM

To her, for I must still regard her
As feminine in her degree,
Who has been my unkind bombarder

Year after year, in grief and glee,
Year after year with oaken tree ;
And yet between whiles my laudator
In terms astonishing to me—
To the Right Reverend The Spectator
I here, a humble dedicator,
Bring the last apples from my tree.

In tones of love, in tones of warning,
She hailed me through my brief career ;
And kiss and buffet, night and morning,
Told me my grandmamma was near ;
Whether she praised me high and clear
Through her unrivalled circulation,
Or, sanctimonious insincere,
She damned me with a misquotation—
A chequered but a sweet relation,
Say, was it not, my granny dear ?

Believe me, granny, altogether
Yours, though perhaps to your surprise.
Oft have you spruced my wounded feather,
Oft brought a light into my eyes—
For notice still the writer cries.
In any civil age or nation,
The book that is not talked of dies.
So that shall be my termination :
Whether in praise or execration,
Still, if you love me, criticise !

BOOK II
IN SCOTS

NOTE

THE human conscience has fled of late the troublesome domain of conduct for what I should have supposed to be the less congenial field of art : there she may now be said to rage, and with special severity in all that touches dialect ; so that in every novel the letters of the alphabet are tortured, and the reader wearied, to commemorate shades of mispronunciation. Now spelling is an art of great difficulty in my eyes, and I am inclined to lean upon the printer, even in common practice, rather than to venture abroad upon new quests. And the Scots tongue has an orthography of its own, lacking neither " authority nor author." Yet the temptation is great to lend a little guidance to the bewildered Englishman. Some simple phonetic artifice might defend your verses from barbarous mishandling, and yet not injure any vested interest. So it seems at first ; but there are rocks ahead. Thus, if I wish the diphthong *ou* to have its proper value, I may write *oor* instead of *our ;* many have done so and lived, and the pillars of the universe remained unshaken. But if I did so, and came presently to *doun*, which is the classical Scots spelling of the English *down*, I should begin to feel uneasy ; and if I went on a little farther, and came to a classical Scots word, like *stour* or *dour* or *clour*, I should know precisely where I was—that is to say, that I was out of sight of land on those high seas of spelling reform in which so many strong swimmers have toiled vainly. To some the situation is exhilarating ; as for me, I give one bubbling cry and sink. The compromise at which I have arrived is indefensible, and I have no thought of trying to defend it. As I have stuck for the most part to the proper spelling, I append a table of some common vowel sounds which no one need consult ; and just to prove that I belong to my age and have in me the stuff of a reformer, I have used modification marks throughout. Thus I can tell myself, not without pride, that I have added a fresh stumbling-block for English readers, and to a page of print in my native tongue have lent a new uncouthness. *Sed non nobis.*

I note again, that among our new dialecticians, the local habitat of every dialect is given to the square mile. I could not emulate this nicety if I desired ; for I simply wrote my Scots as well as I was able, not caring if it hailed from Lauderdale or Angus, from the Mearns or Galloway ; if I had ever heard a good word, I used it without shame ; and when Scots was lacking, or the rhyme jibbed, I was glad (like my betters) to fall back on English. For all that, I own to a friendly feeling for the tongue of Fergusson and of Sir Walter, both Edinburgh men ; and I confess that Burns has always sounded in my ear like something partly foreign. And indeed I am from the Lothians myself ; it is there I heard the language spoken about my childhood ; and it is in the drawling Lothian voice that I repeat it to myself. Let the precisians call my speech that of the Lothians. And if it be not pure, alas ! what matters it ? The day draws near when this illustrious and malleable tongue shall be quite forgotten ; and Burns's Ayrshire, and Dr. MacDonald's Aberdeen-awa', and Scott's brave, metropolitan utterance will be all equally the ghosts of speech. Till then I would love to have my hour as a native Maker, and be read by my own country-folk in our own dying language : an ambition surely rather of the heart than of the head, so restricted as it is in prospect of endurance, so parochial in bounds of space.

TABLE OF COMMON SCOTTISH VOWEL SOUNDS

ae
ai } = open A as in *rare*.

a'
au } = AW as in *law*.
aw

ea = open E as in *mere*, but this with exceptions, as heather
     = heather, wean = wain, lear = lair.

ee
ei } = open E as in *mere*.
ie

oa = open O as in *more*.

ou = doubled O as in *poor*.

ow = OW as in *bower*.

u = doubled O as in *poor*.

ui or ü before R = (say roughly) open A as in *rare*.

ui or ü before any other consonant = (say roughly) close
     I as in *grin*.

y = open I as in *kite*.

i = pretty nearly what you please, much as in English.
     Heaven guide the reader through that labyrinth !
     But in Scots it dodges usually from the short I
     as in *grin*, to the open E as in *mere*. Find and
     blind, I may remark, are pronounced to rhyme
     with the preterite of grin.

I

THE MAKER TO POSTERITY

FAR 'yont amang the years to be,
When a' we think, an' a' we see,
An' a' we luve, 's been dung ajee *knocked aside*
    By time's rouch shouther, *shoulder*
An' what was richt and wrang for me
    Lies mangled throu'ther, *all together*

It's possible—it's hardly mair—
That some ane, ripin' after lear— *groping after learning*
Some auld professor or young heir,
    If still there's either—
May find an' read me, an' be sair
    Perplexed, puir brither !

" *What tongue does your auld bookie speak ?* "
  He'll spier ; an' I, his mou' to steik : *ask / close*
" *No bein' fit to write in Greek,*
  I wrote in Lallan, *Lowlands*
Dear to my heart as the peat-reek, *smoke*
  Auld as Tantallon.

" *Few spak it then, an' noo there's nane.*
  My puir auld sangs lie a' their lane,
  Their sense, that aince was braw an' plain,
    Tint a'thegither, *lost*
  Like runes upon a standin' stane
    Amang the heather.

" *But think not you the brae to speel ;* *hill to climb*
  You, tae, maun chow the bitter peel ;
  For a' your lear, for a' your skeel,

101

> *Ye're nane sae lucky;*
> *An' things are mebbe waur than weel*
> *For you, my buckie.*

may be

> " *The hale concern (baith hens an' eggs,*
> *Baith books an' writers, stars an' clegs)*
> *Noo stachers upon lowsent legs,*
> *An' wears awa';*
> *The tack o' mankind, near the dregs,*
> *Rins unco law.*

horse-flies
staggers,
loosened

lease of mankind
very low

> " *Your book, that in some braw new tongue*
> *Ye wrote or prentit, preached or sung,*
> *Will still be just a bairn, an' young*
> *In fame an' years,*
> *Whan the hale planet's guts are dung*
> *About your ears;*

> " *An' you, sair gruppin' to a spar*
> *Or whammled wi' some bleezin' star,*
> *Cryin' to ken whaur deil ye are,*
> *Hame, France, or Flanders—*
> *Whang sindry like a railway car*
> *An' flie in danders.*"

overturned

fly asunder
cinders

II

ILLE TERRARUM

> FRAE nirly, nippin', Eas'lan' breeze,
> Frae Norlan' snaw, an' haar o' seas,
> Weel happit in your gairden trees,
>   A bonny bit,
> Atween the muckle Pentland's knees,
>   Secure ye sit

pinching
fog

> Beeches an' aiks entwine their theek,
> An' firs, a stench, auld-farrant clique.

oaks, thatch
staunch,
old-fashioned

A' simmer day, your chimleys reek,
    Couthy an' bien ;   comfortable and well-to-do
An' here an' there your windies keek
    Amang the green.

A pickle plats an' paths an' posies,
A wheen auld gillyflowers an' roses :   few
A ring o' wa's the hale encloses
    Frae sheep or men ;.
An' there the auld housie beeks an' dozes,   basks
    A' by her lane.   by herself

The gairdner crooks his weary back
A' day in the pitaty-track,
Or mebbe stops a while to crack
    Wi' Jane the cook,
Or at some buss, worm-eaten-black,   bush
    To gie a look.

Frae the high hills the curlew ca's ;
The sheep gang baaing by the wa's ;
Or whiles a clan o' roosty craws
    Cangle thegither ;
The wild bees seek the gairden raws,
    Weariet wi' heather.

Or in the gloamin' douce an' grey
The sweet-throat mavis tunes her lay ;
The herd comes linkin' doun the brae ;   tripping
    An' by degrees
The muckle siller müne maks way
    Amang the trees.

Here aft hae I, wi' sober heart,
For meditation sat apairt,
When orra loves or kittle art   various, ticklish
    Perplexed my mind ;
Here socht a balm for ilka smart   every
    O' humankind.

cornered alone

Here aft, weel neukit by my lane,
Wi' Horace, or perhaps Montaigne,
The mornin' hours hae come an' gane
    Abüne my heid—

pebble

I wadna gi'en a chucky-stane
    For a' I'd read.

But noo the auld city, street by street,
An' winter fu' o' snaw an' sleet,

vagrant
roving

A while shut in my gangrel feet
    An' goavin' mettle ;

swept hearth

Noo is the soopit ingle sweet,
    An' liltin' kettle.

An' noo the winter winds complain ;

mud, every
draggled wench,
untidy child

Cauld lies the glaur in ilka lane ;
On draigled hizzie, tautit wean
    An' drucken lads,
In the mirk nicht, the winter rain
    Dribbles an' blads.

Whan bugles frae the Castle rock,

doleful
chilly

An' beaten drums wi' dowie shock,
Wauken, at cauld-rife sax o'clock,
    My chitterin' frame,
I mind me on the kintry cock,
    The kintry hame.

shelter

I mind me on yon bonny bield ;
An' Fancy traivels far afield
To gaither a' that gairdens yield
    O' sun an' Simmer :

downcast lad
jade

To hearten up a dowie chield,
    Fancy's the limmer !

III

WHEN aince Aprile has fairly come,

build

An' birds may bigg in winter's lum,
    An' pleisure's spreid for a' and some

O' whatna state,
Love, wi' her auld recruitin' drum,
    Than taks the gate.

The heart plays dunt wi' main an' micht;
The lasses' een are a' sae bricht,
Their dresses are sae braw an' ticht,
    The bonny birdies !—
Puir winter virtue at the sicht
    Gangs heels ower hurdies.   heels over head

An' aye as love frae land to land
Tirls the drum wi' eident hand,   diligent
A' men collect at her command,
    Toun-bred or land'art,
An' follow in a denty band
    Her gaucy standart.   stately

An' I, wha sang o' rain an' snaw,
An' weary winter weel awa',
Noo busk me in a jacket braw,
    An' tak my place
I' the ram-stam, harum-scarum raw,
    Wi' smilin' face.

IV

A MILE AN' A BITTOCK

A MILE an' a bittock, a mile or twa,
Abüne the burn, ayont the law,   hill
Davie an' Donal' an' Cherlie an' a',
    An' the müne was shinin' clearly !

Ane went hame wi' the ither, an' then
The ither went hame wi' the ither twa men,
An' baith wad return him the service again,
    An' the müne was shinin' clearly !

The clocks were chappin' in house an' ha',
Eleeven, twal' an' ane an' twa;
An' the guidman's face was turnt to the wa',
    An' the müne was shinin' clearly!

from over   A wind got up frae affa the sea,
It blew the stars as clear's could be,
It blew in the een of a' o' the three,
    An' the müne was shinin' clearly!

part   Noo, Davie was first to get sleep in his head,
" The best o' frien's maun twine," he said;
" I'm weariet, an' here I'm awa' to my bed."
    An' the müne was shinin' clearly!

Twa o' them walkin' an' crackin' their lane,
The mornin' licht cam grey an' plain,—
chirruped   An' the birds they yammert on stick an' stane.
    An' the müne was shinin' clearly!

O years ayont, O years awa',
My lads, ye'll mind whate'er befa'—
shelter, hill   My lads, ye'll mind on the bield o' the law,
    When the müne was shinin' clearly!

V

Lothian   A LOWDEN SABBATH MORN

THE clinkum-clank o' Sabbath bells
cawing   Noo to the hoastin' rookery swells,
low   Noo faintin' laigh in shady dells,
    Sounds far an' near,
An' through the simmer kintry tells
    Its tale o' cheer.

An' noo, to that melodious play,
A' deidly awn the quiet sway—
A' ken their solemn holiday,

Bestial an' human,
The singin' lintie on the brae,   **linnet**
    The restin' plou'man.

He, mair than a' the lave o' men,   **rest**
His week completit joys to ken ;
Half-dressed, he daunders out an' in,   **saunters**
    Perplext wi' leisure ;
An' his raxt limbs he'll rax again   **stretched**
    Wi' painfü' pleesure.

The steerin' mither strang afit
Noo shoos the bairnies but a bit ;
Noo cries them ben,[1] their Sinday shüit
    To scart upon them,
Or sweeties in their pooch to pit,
    Wi' blessin's on them.

The lasses, clean frae tap to taes,
Are busked in crunklin' underclaes ;
The gartened hose, the weel-filled stays,
    The nakit shift,
A' bleached on bonny greens for days,
    An' white's the drift.

An' noo to face the kirkward mile :
The guidman's hat o' dacent style,
The blackit shoon, we noo maun fyle   **shoes, soil**
    As white's the miller :
A waefü' peety tae, to spile
    The warth o' siller.

Our Marg'et, aye sae keen to crack,
Douce-stappin' in the stoury track,   **dusty**
Her emeralt goun a' kiltit back
    Frae snawy coats,
White-ankled, leads the kirkward pack
    Wi' Dauvit Groats.

[1] " But "—the outer room, " ben "—the inner room of a two-roomed cottage.

a little behind A thocht ahint, in runkled breeks,
                A' spiled wi' lyin' by for weeks,
hooks on to   The guidman follows closs, an' cleiks
comely   The sonsie missis ;
                His sarious face at aince bespeaks
                    The day that this is.

                And aye an' while we nearer draw
                To whaur the kirkton lies alaw,
                Mair neebours, comin' saft an' slaw
                    Frae here an' there,
drive   The thicker thrang the gate an' caw
dust   The stour in air.

                But hark ! the bells frae nearer clang ;
                To rowst the slaw their sides they bang ;
                An' see ! black coats a'ready thrang
                    The green kirkyaird ;
gate, plunge   And at the yett, the chestnuts spang
                    That brocht the laird

                The solemn elders at the plate
                Stand drinkin' deep the pride o' state :
solemn   The practised hands as gash an' great
                    As Lords o' Session ;
diffident   The later named, a wee thing blate
                    In their expression.

                The prentit stanes that mark the deid,
                Wi' lengthened lip, the sarious read ;
                Syne wag a moraleesin' heid,
                    An' then an' there
limping   Their hirplin' practice an' their creed
                    Try hard to square.

                It's here our Merren lang has lain,
west of   A wee bewast the table-stane ;
                An' yon's the grave o' Sandy Blane ;

An' further ower,
The mither's brithers, dacent men !
Lie a' the fower.

Here the guidman sall bide awee
To dwall amang the deid ; to see
Auld faces clear in fancy's e'e :
  Belike to hear
Auld voices fa'in' saft an' slee
  On fancy's ear.

Thus, on the day o' solemn things,
The bell that in the steeple swings
To fauld a scaittered faim'ly rings
  Its walcome screed ;
An' just a wee thing nearer brings
  The quick an' deid.

But noo the bell is ringin' in ;
To tak their places, folk begin ;
The minister himsel' will shüne
  Be up the gate,
Filled fu' wi' clavers about sin   talk
  An' man's estate.

The tünes are up—*French*, to be shüre.
The faithfü' *French*, an' twa-three mair ;
The auld prezentor, hoastin' sair,   coughing
  Wales out the portions,   chooses
An' yirks the tüne into the air
  Wi' queer contortions.

Follows the prayer, the readin' next,
An' than the fisslin' for the text—
The twa-three last to find it, vext
  But kind o' proud ;
An' than the peppermints are raxed,   reached
  An' southernwood.

For noo's the time whan pows are seen [*heads*]
Nid-noddin' like a mandareen ;
When tenty mithers stap a preen [*watchful, stick a pin*]
    In sleepin' weans ; [*children*]
An' nearly half the parochine [*parish*]
    Forget their pains.

There's just a waukrif twa or three : [*wakeful*]
Thrawn commentautors sweer to 'gree, [*stubborn*]
Weans glowrin' at the bumlin' bee
    On windie-glasses,
Or lads that tak a keek a-glee [*sidelong peep*]
    At sonsie lasses. [*comely*]

Himsel', meanwhile, frae whaur he cocks
An' bobs belaw the soundin'-box,
The treesures of his words unlocks
    Wi' prodigality,
An' deals some unco' dingin' knocks
    To infidality.

Wi' sappy unction, hoo he burkes
The hopes o' men that trust in works,
Expounds the fau'ts o' ither kirks,
    An' shaws the best o' them
No' muckle better than mere Turks,
    When a's confessed o' them.

Bethankit ! what a bonny creed !
What mair would ony Christian need ?—
The braw words rumm'le ower his heid,
    Nor steer the sleeper ;
And in their restin' graves, the deid
    Sleep aye the deeper.

NOTE.—It may be guessed by some that I had a certain parish
in my eye, and this makes it proper I should add a word of dis-
clamation. In my time there have been two ministers in that
parish. Of the first I have a special reason to speak well, even
had there been any to think ill. The second I have often met

ın private and long (in the due phrase) "sat under" in his
church, and neither here nor there have I heard an unkind or
ugly word upon his lips. The preacher of the text had thus no
original in that particular parish; but when I was a boy, he
might have been observed in many others; he was then (like the
schoolmaster) abroad; and by recent advices it would seem he
has not yet entirely disappeared.—[R. L. S.]

VI

THE SPAEWIFE

Fortune teller

O, I wad like to ken—to the beggar-wife says I—
Why chops are guid to brander and nane sae guid
  to fry. *grill*
An' siller, that's sae braw to keep, is brawer still
  to gi'e.
—*It's gey an' easy speirin'*, says the beggar-wife to *very easy asking*
  me.

O, I wad like to ken—to the beggar-wife says I—
Hoo a' things come to be whaur we find them when
  we try,
The lasses in their claes an' the fishes in the sea.
—*It's gey an' easy speirin'*, says the beggar-wife to
  me.

O, I wad like to ken—to the beggar-wife says I—
Why lads are a' to sell an' lasses a' to buy;
An' naebody for dacency but barely twa or three.
—*It's gey an' easy speirin'*, says the beggar-wife to
  me.

O, I wad like to ken—to the beggar-wife says I—
Gin death's as shüre to men as killin' is to kye, *cows*
Why God has filled the yearth sae fu' o' tasty things
  to pree. *taste*
—*It's gey an' easy speirin'*, says the beggar-wife to
  me.

O, I wad like to ken—to the beggar-wife says I—
The reason o' the cause an' the wherefore o' the
    why,
Wi' mony anither riddle brings the tear into my
    e'e.
—It's gey an' easy speirin', says the beggar-wife to
    me.

VII

THE BLAST—1875

It's rainin'. Weet's the gairden sod,
    Weet the lang roads whaur gangrels plod—
    A maist unceevil thing o' God
        In mid July—
If ye'll just curse the sneckdraw, dod !
        An' sae wull I !

He's a braw place in Heev'n, ye ken,
    An' lea's us puir, forjaskit men
    Clamjamfried in the but and ben
        He ca's the earth—
    A wee bit inconvenient den
        No muckle worth ;

An' whiles, at orra times, keeks out,
    Sees what puir mankind are about ;
    An' if He can, I've little doubt,
        Upsets their plans ;
    He hates a' mankind, brainch and root,
        An' a' that's man's.

An' whiles, whan they tak' heart again,
    An' life o' the sun looks braw an' plain,
    Doun comes a jaw o' droukin' rain
        Upon their honours—
God sends a spate out-ower the plain,
        Or mebbe thun'ers.

Marginal glosses:
vagrants
tricky fellow
jaded, pinched
peeps
plump, soaking
flood

Lord safe us, life's an unco thing!   wonderful
Simmer an' Winter, Yule an' Spring,
The damned, dour-heartit seasons bring   stubborn
    A feck o' trouble.   lot
I wadna try't to be a king—
    No, nor for double.

But since we're in it, willy-nilly,
We maun be watchfü', wise an' skilly,
An' no mind ony ither billy,
    Lassie nor God.
But drink—that's my best counsel till 'e:
    Sae tak' the nod.

VIII

THE COUNTERBLAST—1886

My bonny man, the warld, it's true,
Was made for neither me nor you;
It's just a place to warstle through,   wrestle
    As Job confessed o't;
And aye the best that we'll can do
    Is mak' the best o't.

There's rowth o' wrang, I'm free to say: plenty
The simmer brunt, the winter blae,
The face of earth a' fyled wi' clay   dirtied
    An' dour wi' chuckies,   pebbles
An' life a rough an' land'art play
    For country buckies.

An' food's anither name for clart;   dirt
An' beasts an' brambles bite an' scart;
An' what would we be like, my heart!
    If bared o' claethin'?
—Aweel, I canna mend your cart:
    It's that or naethin'.

I

lot

A feck o' folk frae first to last
Have through this queer experience passed ;
Twa-three, I ken, just damn and blast
    The hale transaction ;
But twa-three ithers, east an' wast,
    Fand satisfaction.

Whaur braid the briery muirs expand,
A waefü' an' a weary land,
The bumble-bees, a gowden band,
    Are blithely hingin' ;

cheerful
lark

An' there the canty wanderer fand
    The laverock singin'.

Trout in the burn grow great as herr'n' ;
The simple sheep can find their fair'n' ;
The wind blaws clean about the cairn

fresh

    Wi' caller air ;
The muircock an' the barefit bairn
    Are happy there.

shelters
trouble

Sic-like the howes o' life to some :
Green loans whaur they ne'er fash their thumb,
But mark the muckle winds that come,

sweeping

    Soopin' an' cool,
Or hear the powrin' burnie drum

chaffinch's

    In the shilfa's pool.

The evil wi' the guid they tak' ;
They ca' a grey thing grey, no black ;

steep hill

To a steigh brae a stubborn back
    Addressin' daily ;

unsheltered

An' up the rude, unbieldy track
    O' life, gang gaily.

What you would like's a palace ha',
Or Sinday parlour dink an' braw

neat

Wi' a' things ordered in a raw
    By denty leddies.
Weel, then, ye canna hae't : that's a'
    That to be said is.

An' since at life ye've ta'en the grue,   *distaste*
An' winna blithely hirsle through,   *scramble*
Ye've fund the very thing to do—
    That's to drink speerit;
An' shüne we'll hear the last o' you—
    An' blithe to hear it!

The shoon ye coft, the life ye lead,   *shoes, buy*
Ithers will heir when aince ye're deid;
They'll heir your tasteless bite o' breid,
    An' find it sappy;
They'll to your dulefü' house succeed,
    An' there be happy.

As whan a glum an' fractious wean   *child*
Has sat an' sullened by his lane
Till, wi' a rowstin' skelp, he's ta'en   *slap*
    An' shoo'd to bed—   *chased*
The ither bairns a' fa' to play'n',
    As gleg's a gled.   *lively, hawk*

IX

THE COUNTERBLAST IRONICAL

It's strange that God should fash to frame   *trouble*
    The yearth and lift sae hie,   *heaven*
An' clean forget to explain the same
    To a gentleman like me.

Thae gutsy, donnered ither folk,   *greedy, stupid*
    Their weird they weel may dree;
But why present a pig in a poke
    To a gentleman like me?

Thae ither folk their parritch eat
    An' sup their sugared tea;
But the mind is no' to be wyled wi' meat
    Wi' a gentleman like me.

Thae ither folk, they court their joes
    At gloamin' on the lea ;
But they're made of a commoner clay, I suppose,
    Than a gentleman like me.

Thae ither folk, for richt or wrang,
    They suffer, bleed, or dee ;
But a' thir things are an emp'y sang
    To a gentleman like me.

It's a different thing that I demand,
    Tho' humble as can be—
A statement fair in my Maker's hand
    To a gentleman like me :

A clear account writ fair an' broad,
    An' a plain apologie ;
Or the deevil a ceevil word to God
    From a gentleman like me.

X

THEIR LAUREATE TO AN ACADEMY
CLASS DINNER CLUB

DEAR Thamson class, whaure'er I gang
It aye comes ower me wi' a spang :
" *Lordsake ! thae Thamson lads—(deil hang
        Or else Lord mend them) !—*
unlucky   *An' that wanchancy annual sang
        I ne'er can send them !* "

        Straucht, at the name, a trusty tyke,
snarls My conscience girrs ahint the dyke ;
fuss   Straucht on my hinderlands I fyke
            To find a rhyme t' ye ;
        Pleased—although mebbe no' pleased-like—
            To gie my time t' ye.

" *Weel*," an' says you, wi' heavin' breist,
" *Sae far, sae guid, but what's the neist?*
Yearly we gaither to the feast,
    A' hopefü' men—
Yearly we skelloch ' Hang the beast—   cry out
    Nae sang again ! ' "

My lads, an' what am I to say ?
Ye shürely ken the Muse's way :
Yestreen, as gleg's a tyke—the day,   lively, dog
    Thrawn like a cuddy ;   cross-grained
                            donkey
Her conduc', that to her's a play,
    Deith to a body.

Aft whan I sat an' made my mane,   moan
Aft whan I laboured burd-alane,   an only child
Fishin' for rhymes an' findin' nane,
    Or nane were fit for ye—
Ye judged me cauld's a chucky-stane—   pebble
    No car'n' a bit for ye !

But saw ye ne'er some pingein' bairn   whining
As weak as a pitaty-par'n'—   potato-skin
Less üsed wi' guidin' horse-shoe airn
    Than sterrin' crowdie—   pottage
Packed aff his lane, by moss an' cairn,   by himsel
    To ca' the howdie.   midwife

Wae's me, for the puir callant than !   lad
He wambles like a poke o' bran,   wobbles
An' the lowse rein, as hard's he can,
    Pu's, trem'lin' handit ;
Till, blaff ! upon his hinderlan'
    Behauld him landit.

Sic-like—I awn the weary fac'—
Whan on my muse the gate I tak',
An' see her gleed e'e raxin' back   squinting,
    To keek ahint her ;—   reaching
To me, the brig o' Heev'n gangs **black**   peep
    As blackest winter.

" Lordsake ! we're aff," thinks I, *" but whaur ?*
rock *On what abhorred an' whinny scaur,*
mud *Or whammled in what sea o' glaur,*
    Will she desert me ?
An' will she just disgrace ? or waur—
    Will she no' hurt me ? "

puzzling Kittle the quære ! But at least
troublesome The day I've backed the fashious beast,
spring While she, wi' mony a spang an' reist,
    Flang heels ower bonnet ;
An' a' triumphant—for your feast,
    Hae ! there's your sonnet !

XI

EMBRO HIE KIRK

The Lord Himsel' in former days
chose Waled out the proper tünes for praise
An' named the proper kind o' claes
    For folk to preach in :
Preceese and in the chief o' ways
    Important teachin'.

He ordered a' things late and air' ;
early He ordered folk to stand at prayer
(Although I canna just mind where
    He gave the warnin'),
An' pit pomatum on their hair
    On Sabbath mornin'.

The hale o' life by His commands
Was ordered to a body's hands ;
But see ! this *corpus juris* stands
    By a' forgotten ;
An' God's religion in a lands
    Is deid an' rotten.

While thus the lave o' mankind's lost, rest
O' Scotland still God maks His boast—
Puir Scotland, on whase barren coast
  A score or twa
Auld wives wi' mutches an' a hoast caps, cough
  Still keep His law.

In Scotland, a wheen canty, plain, few
Douce, kintry-leevin' folk retain
The Truth—or did so aince—alane
  Of a' men leevin';
An' noo just twa o' them remain—
  Just Begg an' Niven.[1]

For noo, unfaithfü' to the Lord,
Auld Scotland joins the rebel horde ;
Her human hymn-books on the board
  She noo displays :
An' Embro Hie Kirk's been restored
  In popish ways.

O punctum temporis for action
To a' o' the reformin' faction,
If yet, by ony act or paction,
  Thocht, word, or sermon,
This dark an' damnable transaction
  Micht yet determine !

For see—as Doctor Begg explains—
Hoo easy 't's düne ! a pickle weans, a few children
Wha in the Hie Street gaither stanes
  By his instruction,
The uncovenantit, pentit panes painted
  Ding to destruction.

[1] Two Scotsmen, celebrated for their pronounced Presbyterian orthodoxy.

low, mud
crash

organ

Up, Niven, or ower late—an' dash
Laigh in the glaur that carnal hash ;
Let spires and pews wi' gran' stramash
 Thegither fa' ;
The rumlin' kist o' whustles smash
 In pieces sma'.

heavy

totter, tumble
unlucky

chamber

Noo choose ye out a walie hammer ;
About the knottit buttress clam'er ;
Alang the steep roof stoyt an' stammer,
 A gate mischancy ;
On the aul' spire, the bells' hie cha'mer,
 Dance your bit dancie.

Ding, devel, dunt, destroy, an' ruin,
Wi' carnal stanes the square bestrewin',
Till your loud chaps frae Kyle to Fruin,
 Frae Hell to Heeven,
Tell the guid wark that baith are doin'—
 Baith Begg an' Niven.

XII

THE SCOTSMAN'S RETURN FROM ABROAD

(IN A LETTER FROM MR. THOMSON TO MR. JOHNSTONE)

many strange
things

quick, observing
eyes

every

waandering
pith

IN mony a foreign pairt I've been,
An' mony an unco ferlie seen,
Since, Mr. Johnstone, you and I
Last walkit upon Cocklerye.
Wi' gleg, observant een, I pass't
By sea an' land, through East an' Wast,
And still in ilka age an' station
Saw naething but abomination.
In thir uncovenantit lands
The gangrel Scot uplifts his hands
At lack of a' sectarian füsh'n,

An' cauld religious destitütion.
He rins, puir man, frae place to place,
Tries a' their graceless means o' grace,
Preacher on preacher, kirk on kirk—
This yin a stot an' thon a stirk[1]—
A bletherin' clan, no warth a preen,   pin
As bad as Smith of Aiberdeen ![2]

At last, across the weary faem,
Frae far, outlandish pairts I came.
On ilka side o' me I fand
Fresh tokens o' my native land.
Wi' whatna joy I hailed them a'—
The hill-taps standin' raw by raw;
The public house, the Hielan' birks,   United
And a' the bonny U.P. kirks !   Presbyterian
But maistly thee, the bluid o' Scots,
Frae Maidenkirk to John o' Grots,
The king o' drinks, as I conceive it,
Talisker, Isla, or Glenlivet !

For after years wi' a pockmantie   portmanteau
Frae Zanzibar to Alicante,
In mony a fash and sair affliction
I gie't as my sincere conviction—
Of a' their foreign tricks an' pliskies,   mischiefs
I maist abominate their whiskies.
Nae doot, themsel's, they ken it weel,
An' wi' a hash o' leemon peel,
And ice an' siccan filth, they ettle   such, try
The stawsome kind o' goo to settle ;   disgusting,
Sic wersh apothecary's broos wi'   taste insipid
As Scotsmen scorn to fyle their moo's wi'.

[1] "Stot" and "stirk," *lit.* cattle, used to express stupidity.

[2] The late Professor Robertson Smith of Cambridge, formerly of Aberdeen, a leader of the school of advanced Biblical criticism.

An', man, I was a blithe hame-comer
rinsed, tumbler   Whan first I syndit out my rummer
Ye should hae seen me then, wi' care
The less important pairts prepare ;
Syne, weel contentit wi' it a',
plump   Pour in the speerits wi' a jaw !
I didna drink, I didna speak,—
snuffed, smoke   I only snowkit up the reek.
I was sae pleased therein to paidle,
paddled   I sat an' plowtered wi' my ladle

An' blithe was I, the morrow's morn,
saunter   To daunder through the stookit corn,
mishaps   And after a' my strange mishanters,
Sit doun amang my ain dissenters
An', man, it was a joy to me
The pu'pit an' the pews to see,
The pennies dirlin' in the plate,
The elders lookin' on in state ;
An' 'mang the first, as it befell,
Wha should I see, sir, but yoursel' !
I was, and I will no' deny it,
glance   At the first gliff a hantle tryit
To see yoursel' in sic a station—
It seemed a doubtfü' dispensation.
The feelin' was a mere digression ;
For shüne I understood the session,
An' mindin' Aiken an' M'Neil,
I wondered they had düne sae weel.
I saw I had mysel' to blame ;
For had I but remained at hame,
perhaps   Aiblins—though no ava' deservin' 't—
They micht hae named your humble servant.

closed   The kirk was filled, the door was steiked
peeped   Up to the pu'pit ance I keeked ;
I was mair pleased than I can tell—
It was the minister himsel' !

Proud, proud was I to see his face,
After sae long awa' frae grace.
Pleased as I was, I'm no denyin'
Some maitters were not edifyin';
For first I fand—an' here was news !—
Mere hymn-books cockin' in the pews—
A humanised abomination,
Unfit for ony congregation.
Syne, while I still was on the tenter,
I scunnered at the new prezentor ;   shuddered
I thocht him gesterin' an' cauld—
A sair declension frae the auld.
Syne, as though a' the faith was wreckit,
The prayer was not what I'd exspeckit.
Himsel', as it appeared to me,
Was no' the man he üsed to be.
But just as I was growin' vext
He waled a maist judeecious text,   chose
An', launchin' into his prelections,
Swoopt, wi' a skirl, on a' defections.

O what a gale was on my speerit
To hear the p'ints o' doctrine clearit,
And a' the horrors o' damnation
Set furth wi' faithfü' ministration !
Nae shauchlin' testimony here—   shuffling
We were a' damned, an' that was clear.
I owned, wi' gratitude an' wonder,
He was a pleesure to sit under.

XIII

LATE in the nicht in bed I lay,
The winds were at their weary play,
An' turlin' wa's an' skirlin' wae   twirling,
shrieking
     Through Heev'n they battered ;—
On-ding 'o hail, on-blaff o' spray,
     The tempest blattered.

capsized

The masoned house it dinled through;
It dung the ship, it cowped the coo';
The rankit aiks it overthrew,
      Had braved a' weathers;

sea-kites

The strang sea-gleds it took an' blew
      Awa' like feathers.

throes

The thrawes o' fear on a' were shed,
An' the hair rose, an' slumber fled,
An' lichts were lit an' prayers were said
      Through a' the kintry;
An' the cauld terror clum in bed
      Wi' a' an' sindry.

tumultuous
uproar

would have
upset

sold by auction

To hear in the pit-mirk on hie
The brangled collieshangie flie,
The warl', they thocht, wi' land an' sea
      Itsel' wad cowpit;
An' for auld airn, the smashed débris
      By God be rowpit.

Meanwhile frae far Aldeboran,
To folks wi' talescopes in han',
O' ships that cowpit, winds that ran,
      Nae sign was seen,
But the wee warl' in sunshine span

pin

      As bricht's a preen.

sheltered

I, tae, by God's especial grace,
Dwall denty in a bieldy place,
Wi' hosened feet, wi' shaven face,
      Wi' dacent mainners:
      A grand example to the race

slovenly

      O' tautit sinners!

The wind may blaw, the heathen rage,
The deil may start on the rampage;—
The sick in bed, the thief in cage—
      What's a' to me?

cosy

Cosh in my house, a sober sage,
      I sit an' see.

An' whiles the bluid spangs to my bree, *springs, brow*
To lie sae saft, to live sae free,
While better men maun do an' die
    In unco places. *strange*
" *Whaur's God?* " I cry, an' " *Whae is me*
    To hae sic graces? "

I mind the fecht the sailors keep,
But fire or can'le, rest or sleep, *without*
In darkness an' the muckle deep;
    An' mind beside
The herd that on the hills o' sheep
    Has wandered wide.

I mind me on the hoastin' weans— *coughing*
The penny joes on causey-stanes—
The auld folk wi' the crazy banes;
    Baith auld an' puir,
That aye maun thole the winds an' rains, *endure*
    An' labour sair.

An' whiles I'm kind o' pleased a blink,
An' kind o' fleyed forby, to think, *frightened*
For a' my rowth o' meat and drink *plenty*
    An' waste o' crumb,
I'll mebbe have to thole wi' skink *put up with*
    In Kingdom Come. *wish-wash*

For God whan jowes the Judgment-bell,
Wi' His ain Hand, His Leevin' Sel',
Sall ryve the guid (as Prophets tell)
    Frae them that had it;
And in the reamin' pat o' Hell, *frothing*
    The rich be scaddit. *scalded*

O Lord, if this indeed be sae,
Let daw that sair an' happy day! *dawn*
Again' the warl', grawn auld an' grey,
    Up wi' your aixe!
And let the puir enjoy their play—
    I'll thole my paiks. *I'll stand my punishment*

XIV

MY CONSCIENCE

Of a' the ills that flesh can fear,
The loss o' frien's, the lack o' gear,
dog, mare   A yowlin' tyke, a glandered mear,
      A lassie's nonsense—
There's just ae thing I canna bear,
      An' that's my conscience.

Whan day (an' a' excüse) has gane,
An' wark is düne, and duty's plain,
chamber   An' to my chalmer a' my lane
      I creep apairt,
gnawing   My conscience! hoo the yammerin' pain
      Stends to my heart!

A' day wi' various ends in view
harvests   The hairsts o' time I had to pu',
disgust a pig   An' made a hash wad staw a soo,
      Let be a man!—
My conscience! whan my han's were fu',
      Whaur were ye than?

An' there were a' the lures o' life,
There pleesure skirlin' on the fife,
lopping   There anger, wi' the hotchin' knife
      Ground shairp in Hell—
My conscience!—you that's like a wife!—
      Whaur was yoursel'?

I ken it fine: just waitin' here,
To gar the evil waur appear,
besmirch   To clart the guid, confüse the clear,
      Misca' the great,
My conscience! an' to raise a steer
      When a's ower late.

Sic-like, some tyke grawn auld and blind,
Whan thieves brok' through the gear to p'ind   goods to seize
Has lain his dozened length an' grinned   stupefied
    At the disaster;
An' the morn's mornin', wud's the wind,   next morning,
    Yokes on his master.   wild as the wind

XV

TO DOCTOR JOHN BROWN

Whan the dear doctor, dear to a',
Was still amang us here belaw,
I set my pipes his praise to blaw
    Wi' a' my speerit;
But noo, dear Doctor! he's awa'
    An' ne'er can hear it.

By Lyne and Tyne, by Thames and Tees,
By a' the various river Dee's,
In Mars and Manors 'yont the seas
    Or here at hame,
Whaure'er there's kindly folk to please,
    They ken your name.

They ken your name, they ken your tyke,
They ken the honey from your byke;   hive
But mebbe after a' your fyke,   trouble
    (The truth to tell)
It's just your honest Rab they like,
    An' no' yoursel'.

As at the gowff, some canny play'r
Should tee a common ba' wi' care—
Should flourish and deleever fair
    His souple shintie—   hockey-stick
An' the ba' rise into the air,
    A leevin' lintie: linnet

Sae in the game we writers play,
There comes to some a bonny day,

wonder

When a dear ferlie shall repay
    Their years o' strife,
An' like your Rab, their things o' clay,
    Spreid wings o' life.

Ye scarce deserved it, I'm afraid—
You that had never learned the trade,
But just some idle mornin' strayed
    Into the schüle,
An' picked the fiddle up an' played
    Like Neil [1] himsel'.

quick, neat

Your e'e was gleg, your fingers dink;
Ye didna fash yoursel' to think,

trip

But wove, as fast as puss can link,
    Your denty wab :—
Ye stapped your pen into the ink,
    An' there was Rab !

since then
dull, cheerful

Sinsyne, whaure'er your fortune lay
By dowie den, by canty brae,
Simmer an' winter, nicht an' day,
    Rab was aye wi' ye ;
An a' the folk on a' the way
    Were blithe to see ye.

O sir, the gods are kind indeed,
An' hauld ye for an honoured heid,
That for a wee bit clarkit screed
    Sae weel reward ye,
An' lend—puir Rabbie bein' deid—
    His ghaist to guard ye.

For though, whaure'er yoursel' may be,

look a little

We've just to turn an' glisk a wee,
An' Rab at heel we're shüre to see
    Wi' gladsome caper :—

ghost

The bogle of a bogle, he—
    A ghaist o' paper !

[1] Neil Gow, the great Highland fiddler.

And as the auld-farrant hero sees   old-fashioned
In Hell a bogle Hercules,
Pit there the lesser deid to please,
    While he himsel'
Dwalls wi' the muckle gods at ease
    Far raised frae hell :

Sae the true Rabbie far has gane
On kindlier business o' his ain
Wi' aulder frien's ; an' his breist-bane
    An' stumpie tailie,
He birstles at a new hearth-stane   toasts
    By James and Ailie.

XVI

It's an owercome sooth for age an' youth   true refrain
    And it brooks wi' nae denial,
That the dearest friends are the auldest friends,
    And the young are just on trial.

There's a rival bauld wi' young an' auld
    And it's him that has bereft me ;
For the sürest friends are the auldest friends
    And the maist o' mine's hae left me.

There are kind hearts still, for friends to fill
    And fools to take and break them ;
But the nearest friends are the auldest friends
    And the grave's the place to seek them.

SONGS OF TRAVEL AND OTHER VERSES

WRITTEN
PRINCIPALLY IN THE SOUTH SEAS
1888-1894

SONGS OF TRAVEL

SONGS OF TRAVEL

I

THE VAGABOND

(TO AN AIR OF SCHUBERT)

GIVE to me the life I love,
  Let the lave go by me,
Give the jolly heaven above
  And the byway nigh me.
Bed in the bush with stars to see,
  Bread I dip in the river—
There's the life for a man like me,
  There's the life for ever.

Let the blow fall soon or late,
  Let what will be o'er me ;
Give the face of earth around
  And the road before me.
Wealth I seek not, hope nor love,
  Nor a friend to know me ;
All I seek, the heaven above
  And the road below me.

Or let autumn fall on me
  Where afield I linger,
Silencing the bird on tree,
  Biting the blue finger :
White as meal the frosty field—
  Warm the fireside haven—
Not to autumn will I yield,
  Not to winter even !

Let the blow fall soon or late,
  Let what will be o'er me ;
Give the face of earth around,
  And the road before me.
Wealth I ask not, hope nor love,
  Nor a friend to know me.
All I ask, the heaven above,
  And the road below me.

II

YOUTH AND LOVE

I

ONCE only by the garden gate
  Our lips we joined and parted.
I must fulfil an empty fate
  And travel the uncharted.

Hail and farewell ! I must arise,
  Leave here the fatted cattle,
And paint on foreign lands and skies
  My Odyssey of battle.

The untented Kosmos my abode,
  I pass, a wilful stranger :
My mistress still the open road
  And the bright eyes of danger.

Come ill or well, the cross, the crown,
  The rainbow or the thunder,
I fling my soul and body down
  For God to plough them under.

III

YOUTH AND LOVE

II

To the heart of youth the world is a highwayside.
  Passing for ever, he fares ; and on either hand,

Deep in the gardens golden pavilions hide,
   Nestle in orchard bloom, and far on the level land
Call him with lighted lamp in the eventide.

Thick as the stars at night when the moon is down,
   Pleasures assail him. He to his nobler fate
Fares ; and but waves a hand as he passes on,
   Cries but a wayside word to her at the garden gate,
Sings but a boyish stave and his face is gone.

IV

THE UNFORGOTTEN

I

IN dreams, unhappy, I behold you stand
   As heretofore :
The unremembered tokens in your hand
   Avail no more.

No more the morning glow, no more the grace,
   Enshrines, endears.
Cold beats the light of time upon your face
   And shows your tears.

He came, he went. Perchance you wept a while
   And then forgot.
Ah me ! but he that left you with a smile
   Forgets you not.

V

THE UNFORGOTTEN

II

SHE rested by the Broken Brook
   She drank of Weary Well,
She moved beyond my lingering look,
   Ah, whither none can tell !

She came, she went. In other lands,
  Perchance in fairer skies,
Her hands shall cling with other hands,
  Her eyes to other eyes.

She vanished. In the sounding town,
  Will she remember too?
Will she recall the eyes of brown
  As I recall the blue?

VI

THE infinite shining heavens
  Rose and I saw in the night
Uncountable angel stars
  Showering sorrow and light.

I saw them distant as heaven,
  Dumb and shining and dead,
And the idle stars of the night
  Were dearer to me than bread.

Night after night in my sorrow
  The stars stood over the sea,
Till lo! I looked in the dusk
  And a star had come down to me.

VII

PLAIN as the glistering planets shine
  When winds have cleaned the skies,
Her love appeared, appealed for mine,
  And wantoned in her eyes.

Clear as the shining tapers burned
  On Cytherea's shrine,
Those brimming, lustrous beauties turned,
  And called and conquered mine.

The beacon-lamp that Hero lit
　　No fairer shone on sea,
No plainlier summoned will and wit,
　　Than hers encouraged me.

I thrilled to feel her influence near,
　　I struck my flag at sight.
Her starry silence smote my ear
　　Like sudden drums at night.

I ran as, at the cannon's roar,
　　The troops the ramparts man—
As in the holy house of yore
　　The willing Eli ran.

Here, lady, lo ! that servant stands
　　You picked from passing men,
And should you need nor heart nor hands
　　He bows and goes again.

VIII

To you, let snow and roses
　　And golden locks belong :
These are the world's enslavers,
　　Let these delight the throng.
For her of duskier lustre,
　　Whose favour still I wear,
The snow be in her kirtle,
　　The rose be in her hair !

The hue of highland rivers
　　Careering, full and cool,
From sable on to golden,
　　From rapid on to pool—
The hue of heather-honey,
　　The hue of honey-bees,
Shall tinge her golden shoulder,
　　Shall gild her tawny knees.

IX

LET Beauty awake in the morn from beautiful dreams,
        Beauty awake from rest !
        Let Beauty awake
        For Beauty's sake
In the hour when the birds awake in the brake
        And the stars are bright in the west !

Let Beauty awake in the eve from the slumber of day,
        Awake in the crimson eve !
        In the day's dusk end
        When the shades ascend,
Let her wake to the kiss of a tender friend
        To render again and receive !

X

    I KNOW not how it is with you—
        I love the first and last,
    The whole field of the present view,
        The whole flow of the past.

    One tittle of the things that are
        Nor you should change nor I—
    One pebble in our path—one star
        In all our heaven of sky.

    Our lives, and every day and hour,
        One symphony appear :
    One road, one garden—every flower
        And every bramble dear.

XI

I WILL make you brooches and toys for your delight
Of bird-song at morning and star-shine at night.
I will make a palace fit for you and me
Of green days in forests and blue days at sea.

I will make my kitchen, and you shall keep your room,
Where white flows the river and bright blows the broom,
And you shall wash your linen and keep your body white
In rainfall at morning and dewfall at night.

And this shall be for music when no one else is near,
The fine song for singing, the rare song to hear !
That only I remember, that only you admire,
Of the broad road that stretches and the roadside fire.

XII

WE HAVE LOVED OF YORE

(TO AN AIR OF DIABELLI)

BERRIED brake and reedy island,
  Heaven below, and only heaven above,
Through the sky's inverted azure
  Softly swam the boat that bore our love.
      Bright were your eyes as the day ;
      Bright ran the stream,
      Bright hung the sky above.
Days of April, airs of Eden,
  How the glory died through golden hours,
And the shining moon arising,
  How the boat drew homeward filled with flowers !
      Bright were your eyes in the night :
      We have lived, my love—
      O, we have loved, my love.

Frost has bound our flowing river,
  Snow has whitened all our island brake,
And beside the winter fagot
  Joan and Darby doze and dream and wake.
      Still, in the river of dreams,
      Swims the boat of love—
      Hark ! chimes the falling oar !

And again in winter evens
    When on firelight dreaming fancy feeds,
In those ears of agèd lovers
    Love's own river warbles in the reeds.
Love still the past, O, my love !
    We have lived of yore,
    O, we have loved of yore.

XIII

DITTY

(TO AN AIR FROM BACH)

THE cock shall crow
    In the morning grey,
The bugles blow
    At the break of day :
The cock shall sing and the merry bugles ring,
And all the little brown birds sing upon the spray.

The thorn shall blow
    In the month of May,
And my love shall go
    In her holiday array :
But I shall lie in the kirkyard nigh
While all the little brown birds sing upon the spray

XIV

MATER TRIUMPHANS

SON of my woman's body, you go, to the drum and fife,
To taste the colour of love and the other side of life—
From out of the dainty the rude, the strong from out of
    the frail,
Eternally through the ages from the female comes the
    male.

The ten fingers and toes, and the shell-like nail on each,
The eyes blind as gems and the tongue attempting speech ;

Impotent hands in my bosom, and yet they shall wield the
    sword !
Drugged with slumber and milk, you wait the day of the
    Lord.

Infant bridegroom, uncrowned king, unanointed priest,
Soldier, lover, explorer, I see you nuzzle the breast.
You that grope in my bosom shall load the ladies with
    rings,
You, that came forth through the doors, shall burst the
    doors of kings.

XV

BRIGHT is the ring of words
    When the right man rings them,
Fair the fall of songs
    When the singer sings them.
Still they are carolled and said—
    On wings they are carried—
After the singer is dead
    And the maker buried.

Low as the singer lies
    In the field of heather,
Songs of his fashion bring
    The swains together.
And when the west is red
    With the sunset embers,
The lover lingers and sings
    And the maid remembers.

XVI

IN the highlands, in the country places,
Where the old plain men have rosy faces,
    And the young fair maidens
        Quiet eyes ;

Where essential silence cheers and blesses,
And for ever in the hill-recesses
Her more lovely music
        Broods and dies.

O to mount again where erst I haunted;
Where the old red hills are bird-enchanted,
And the low green meadows
        Bright with sward;
And when even dies, the million-tinted,
And the night has come, and planets glinted,
Lo! the valley hollow,
        Lamp-bestarred.

O to dream, O to awake and wander
There, and with delight to take and render,
Through the trance of silence,
        Quiet breath;
Lo! for there, among the flowers and grasses,
Only the mightier movement sounds and passes;
Only winds and rivers,
        Life and death.

XVII

(TO THE TUNE OF WANDERING WILLIE)

HOME no more home to me, whither must I wander?
    Hunger my driver, I go where I must.
Cold blows the winter wind over hill and heather;
    Thick drives the rain, and my roof is in the dust.
Loved of wise men was the shade of my roof-tree.
    The true word of welcome was spoken in the door—
Dear days of old, with the faces in the firelight,
    Kind folks of old, you come again no more.

Home was home then, my dear, full of kindly faces,
    Home was home then, my dear, happy for the child.
Fire and the windows bright glittered on the moorland;
    Song, tuneful song, built a palace in the wild.

Now, when day dawns on the brow of the moorland,
    Lone stands the house, and the chimney-stone is cold.
Lone let it stand, now the friends are all departed,
    The kind hearts, the true hearts, that loved the place of
        old.

Spring shall come, come again, calling up the moor-fowl,
    Spring shall bring the sun and rain, bring the bees and
        flowers ;
Red shall the heather bloom over hill and valley,
    Soft flow the stream through the even-flowing hours ;
Fair the day shine as it shone on my childhood—
    Fair shine the day on the house with open door ;
Birds come and cry there and twitter in the chimney—
    But I go for ever and come again no more.

XVIII

TO DR. HAKE

(ON RECEIVING A COPY OF VERSES)

In the belovèd hour that ushers day,
In the pure dew, under the breaking grey,
One bird, ere yet the woodland quires awake,
With brief réveillé summons all the brake :
Chirp, chirp, it goes ; nor waits an answer long ;
And that small signal fills the grove with song.

Thus on my pipe I breathed a strain or two ;
It scarce was music, but 'twas all I knew.
It was not music, for I lacked the art,
Yet what but frozen music filled my heart ?
Chirp, chirp, I went, nor hoped a nobler strain ;
But Heaven decreed I should not pipe in vain,
For, lo ! not far from there, in secret dale,
All silent, sat an ancient nightingale.
My sparrow notes he heard ; threat awoke ;
And with a tide of song his silence broke.

XIX

TO ——

I KNEW thee strong and quiet like the hills ;
I knew thee apt to pity, brave to endure :
In peace or war a Roman full equipt ;
And just I knew thee, like the fabled kings
Who by the loud sea-shore gave judgment forth,
From dawn to eve, bearded and few of words.
What, what, was I to honour thee ? A child,
A youth in ardour but a child in strength,
Who after virtue's golden chariot-wheels
Runs ever panting, nor attains the goal.
So thought I, and was sorrowful at heart.

Since then my steps have visited that flood
Along whose shore the numerous footfalls cease,
The voices and the tears of life expire.
Thither the prints go down, the hero's way
Trod large upon the sand, the trembling maid's :
Nimrod that wound his trumpet in the wood,
And the poor, dreaming child, hunter of flowers,
That here his hunting closes with the great :
So one and all go down, nor aught returns.

For thee, for us, the sacred river waits ;
For me, the unworthy, thee, the perfect friend.
There Blame desists, there his unfaltering dogs
He from the chase recalls, and homeward rides ;
Yet Praise and Love pass over and go in.
So when, beside that margin, I discard
My more than mortal weakness, and with thee
Through that still land unfearing I advance :
If then at all we keep the touch of joy,
Thou shalt rejoice to find me altered—I,
O Felix, to behold thee still unchanged.

XX

THE morning drum-call on my eager ear
Thrills unforgotten yet ; the morning dew
Lies yet undried along my field of noon.
But now I pause at whiles in what I do,
And count the bell, and tremble lest I hear
(My work untrimmed) the sunset gun too soon.

XXI

I HAVE trod the upward and the downward slope ;
I have endured and done in days before ;
I have longed for all, and bid farewell to hope ;
And I have lived and loved, and closed the door.

XXII

HE hears with gladdened heart the thunder
    Peal, and loves the falling dew ;
He knows the earth above and under—
    Sits and is content to view.

He sits beside the dying ember,
    God for hope and man for friend,
Content to see, glad to remember,
    Expectant of the certain end.

XXIII

THE LOST OCCASION

FAREWELL, fair day and fading light !
The clay-born here, with westward sight,
Marks the huge sun now downward soar.
Farewell. We twain shall meet no more.
K

Farewell. I watch with bursting sigh
My late contemned occasion die.
I linger useless in my tent :
Farewell, fair day, so foully spent !

Farewell, fair day. If any God
At all consider this poor clod,
He who the fair occasion sent
Prepared and placed the impediment.

Let him diviner vengeance take—
Give me to sleep, give me to wake
Girded and shod, and bid me play
The hero in the coming day !

XXIV

IF THIS WERE FAITH

God, if this were enough,
That I see things bare to the buff
And up to the buttocks in mire ;
That I ask nor hope nor hire,
Nut in the husk,
Nor dawn beyond the dusk,
Nor life beyond death :
God, if this were faith ?

Having felt thy wind in my face
Spit sorrow and disgrace,
Having seen thine evil doom
In Golgotha and Khartoum,
And the brutes, the work of thine hands,
Fill with injustice lands
And stain with blood the sea :
If still in my veins the glee
Of the black night and the sun
And the lost battle, run :

If, an adept,
The iniquitous lists I still accept
With joy, and joy to endure and be withstood,
And still to battle and perish for a dream of good :
God, if that were enough ?

If to feel, in the ink of the slough,
And the sink of the mire,
Veins of glory and fire
Run through and transpierce and transpire,
And a secret purpose of glory in every part,
And the answering glory of battle fill my heart ;
To thrill with the joy of girded men
To go on for ever and fail and go on again,
And be mauled to the earth and arise,
And contend for the shade of a word and a thing not seen
      with the eyes :
With the half of a broken hope for a pillow at night
That somehow the right is the right
And the smooth shall bloom from the rough :
Lord, if that were enough ?

XXV

MY WIFE

TRUSTY, dusky, vivid, true,
With eyes of gold and bramble-dew,
Steel-true and blade-straight,
The great artificer
    Made my mate.

Honour, anger, valour, fire ;
A love that life could never tire,
    Death quench or evil stir,
    The mighty master
        Gave to her.

Teacher, tender, comrade, wife,
A fellow-farer true through life,
    Heart-whole and soul-free,
    The august father
        Gave to me.

XXVI

WINTER

IN rigorous hours, when down the iron lane
The redbreast looks in vain
    For hips and haws,
Lo, shining flowers upon my window-pane
    The silver pencil of the winter draws.

When all the snowy hill
And the bare woods are still;
When snipes are silent in the frozen bogs,
    And all the garden garth is whelmed in mire.
Lo, by the hearth, the laughter of the logs—
    More fair than roses, lo, the flowers of fire!

SARANAC LAKE.

XXVII

THE stormy evening closes now in vain,
Loud wails the wind and beats the driving rain,
    While here in sheltered house
    With fire-ypainted walls,
    I hear the wind abroad,
    I hark the calling squalls—
" Blow, blow," I cry, " you burst your cheeks in vain!
Blow, blow," I cry, " my love is home again!"

Yon ship you chase perchance but yesternight
Bore still the precious freight of my delight,

That here in sheltered house
With fire-ypainted walls,
Now hears the wind abroad,
Now harks the calling squalls.
" Blow, blow," I cry, " in vain you rouse the sea,
My rescued sailor shares the fire with me ! "

XXVIII

TO AN ISLAND PRINCESS

SINCE long ago, a child at home,
I read and longed to rise and roam,
Where'er I went, whate'er I willed,
One promised land my fancy filled.
Hence the long roads my home I made
Tossed much in ships : have often laid
Below the uncurtained sky my head,
Rain-deluged and wind-buffeted :
And many a thousand hills I crossed
And corners turned—Love's labour lost.
Till, Lady, to your isle of sun
I came, not hoping ; and, like one
Snatched out of blindness, rubbed my eyes,
And hailed my promised land with cries.

Yes, Lady, here I was at last ;
Here found I all I had forecast :
The long roll of the sapphire sea
That keeps the land's virginity ;
The stalwart giants of the wood
Laden with toys and flowers and food ;
The precious forest pouring out
To compass the whole town about ;
The town itself with streets of lawn,
Loved of the moon, blessed by the dawn,
Where the brown children all the day
Keep up a ceaseless noise of play,

Play in the sun, play in the rain,
Nor ever quarrel or complain ;—
And late at night, in the woods of fruit,
Hark ! do you hear the passing flute ?

I threw one look to either hand,
And knew I was in Fairyland.
And yet one point of being so,
I lacked. For, Lady, (as you know)
Whoever by his might of hand
Won entrance into Fairyland,
Found always with admiring eyes
A Fairy princess kind and wise.

It was not long I waited ; soon
Upon my threshold, in broad noon,
Fair and helpful, wise and good,
The Fairy Princess Moë stood.

TANTIRA, TAHITI, Nov. 5, 1888.

XXIX

TO KALAKAUA

(WITH THE GIFT OF A PEARL)

THE Silver Ship, my King—that was her name
In the bright islands whence your fathers came—
The Silver Ship, at rest from winds and tides,
Below your palace in your harbour rides :
And the seafarers, sitting safe on shore,
Like eager merchants count their treasures o'er.
One gift they find, one strange and lovely thing,
Now doubly precious since it pleased a king.

The right, my liege, is ancient as the lyre
For bards to give to kings what kings admire.
'Tis mine to offer for Apollo's sake ;
And since the gift is fitting, yours to take.
To golden hands the golden pearl I bring :
The ocean jewel to the island king.

HONOLULU, Feb. 3, 1889.

XXX

TO PRINCESS KAIULANI

[Written in April to Kaiulani in the April of her age; and at Waikiki, within easy walk of Kaiulani's banyan! When she comes to my land and her father's, and the rain beats upon the window (as I fear it will), let her look at this page; it will be like a weed gathered and pressed at home; and she will remember her own islands, and the shadow of the mighty tree; and she will hear the peacocks screaming in the dusk and the wind blowing in the palms; and she will think of her father sitting there alone.—R. L. S.]

FORTH from her land to mine she goes,
The island maid, the island rose,
Light of heart and bright of face :
The daughter of a double race.

Her islands here, in Southern sun,
Shall mourn their Kaiulani gone,
And I, in her dear banyan shade,
Look vainly for my little maid.

But our Scots islands far away
Shall glitter with unwonted day,
And cast for once their tempests by
To smile in Kaiulani's eye.

HONOLULU.

XXXI

TO MOTHER MARYANNE

To see the infinite pity of this place,
The mangled limb, the devastated face,
The innocent sufferer smiling at the rod—
A fool were tempted to deny his God.
He sees, he shrinks. But if he gaze again,
Lo, beauty springing from the breast of pain !
He marks the sisters on the mournful shores ;
And even a fool is silent and adores.

GUEST HOUSE, KALAWAO, MOLOKAI.

XXXII

IN MEMORIAM, E. H.

I KNEW a silver head was bright beyond compare,
I knew a queen of toil with a crown of silver hair.
Garland of valour and sorrow, of beauty and renown,
Life, that honours the brave, crowned her himself with the
    crown.

The beauties of youth are frail, but this was a jewel of age.
Life, that delights in the brave, gave it himself for a gage.
Fair was the crown to behold, and beauty its poorest part—
At once the scar of the wound and the order pinned on
    the heart.

The beauties of man are frail, and the silver lies in the dust,
And the queen that we call to mind sleeps with the brave
    and the just ;
Sleeps with the weary at length ; but, honoured and ever
    fair,
Shines in the eye of the mind the crown of the silver hair.

HONOLULU.

XXXIII

TO MY WIFE

(A FRAGMENT)

LONG must elapse ere you behold again
Green forest frame the entry of the lane—
The wild lane with the bramble and the briar,
The year-old cart-tracks perfect in the mire,
The wayside smoke, perchance, the dwarfish huts,
And ramblers' donkey drinking from the ruts :—
Long ere you trace how deviously it leads,
Back from man's chimneys and the bleating meads
To the woodland shadow, to the silvan hush,
When but the brooklet chuckles in the brush—

Back from the sun and bustle of the vale
To where the great voice of the nightingale
Fills all the forest like a single room,
And all the banks smell of the golden broom ;
So wander on until the eve descends,
And back returning to your firelit friends,
You see the rosy sun, despoiled of light,
Hung, caught in thickets, like a schoolboy's kite.

Here from the sea the unfruitful sun shall rise,
Bathe the bare deck and blind the unshielded eyes ;
The allotted hours aloft shall wheel in vain
And in the unpregnant ocean plunge again.
Assault of squalls that mock the watchful guard,
And pluck the bursting canvas from the yard,
And senseless clamour of the calm, at night
Must mar your slumbers. By the plunging light,
In beetle-haunted, most unwomanly bower
Of the wild-swerving cabin, hour by hour . . .

SCHOONER *Equator.*

XXXIV

TO THE MUSE

RESIGN the rhapsody, the dream,
    To men of larger reach ;
Be ours the quest of a plain theme,
    The piety of speech.

As monkish scribes from morning break
    Toiled till the close of light,
Nor thought a day too long to make
    One line or letter bright :

We also with an ardent mind,
    Time, wealth, and fame forgot,
Our glory in our patience find,
    And skim, and skim the pot :

Till last, when round the house we hear
    The evensong of birds,
One corner of blue heaven appear
    In our clear well of words.

Leave, leave it then, muse of my heart !
    Sans finish and sans frame,
Leave unadorned by needless art
    The picture as it came.

APEMAMA.

XXXV
TO MY OLD FAMILIARS

Do you remember—can we e'er forget ?—
How, in the coiled perplexities of youth,
In our wild climate, in our scowling town,
We gloomed and shivered, sorrowed, sobbed and
    feared ?
The belching winter wind, the missile rain,
The rare and welcome silence of the snows,
The laggard morn, the haggard day, the night,
The grimy spell of the nocturnal town,
Do you remember ?—Ah, could one forget !

As when the fevered sick that all night long
Listed the wind intone, and hear at last
The ever-welcome voice of chanticleer
Sing in the bitter hour before the dawn,—
With sudden ardour, these desire the day :
So sang in the gloom of youth the bird of hope ;
So we, exulting, hearkened and desired.
For, lo ! as in the palace porch of life
We huddled with chimeras, from within—
How sweet to hear !—the music swelled and fell,
And through the breach of the revolving doors
What dreams of splendour blinded us and fled !

I have since then contended and rejoiced;
Amid the glories of the house of life
Profoundly entered, and the shrine beheld:
Yet when the lamp from my expiring eyes
Shall dwindle and recede, the voice of love
Fall insignificant on my closing ears,
What sound shall come but the old cry of the
          wind
In our inclement city? what return
But the image of the emptiness of youth,
Filled with the sound of footsteps and that voice
Of discontent and rapture and despair?
So, as in darkness, from the magic lamp,
The momentary pictures gleam and fade
And perish, and the night resurges—these
Shall I remember, and then all forget.

APEMAMA.

XXXVI

THE tropics vanish, and meseems that I,
From Halkerside, from topmost Allermuir,
Or steep Caerketton, dreaming gaze again.
Far set in fields and woods, the town I see
Spring gallant from the shallows of her smoke,
Cragged, spired, and turreted, her virgin fort
Beflagged. About, on seaward-drooping hills,
New folds of city glitter. Last, the Forth
Wheels ample waters set with sacred isles,
And populous Fife smokes with a score of towns

There, on the sunny frontage of a hill,
Hard by the house of kings, repose the dead,
My dead, the ready and the strong of word.
Their works, the salt-encrusted, still survive;
The sea bombards their founded towers; the night
Thrills pierced with their strong lamps. The arti-
          ficers,
One after one, here in this grated cell,
Where the rain erases and the rust consumes,

Fell upon lasting silence. Continents
And continental oceans intervene ;
A sea uncharted, on a lampless isle,
Environs and confines their wandering child
In vain. The voice of generations dead
Summons me, sitting distant, to arise,
My numerous footsteps nimbly to retrace,
And, all mutation over, stretch me down
In that denoted city of the dead.

APEMAMA.

XXXVII

TO S. C.[1]

I HEARD the pulse of the besieging sea
Throb far away all night. I heard the wind
Fly crying and convulse tumultuous palms.
I rose and strolled. The isle was all bright sand,
And flailing fans and shadows of the palm ;
The heaven all moon and wind and the blind vault
The keenest planet slain, for Venus slept.
    The king, my neighbour, with his host of wives,
Slept in the precinct of the palisade ;
Where single, in the wind, under the moon,
Among the slumbering cabins, blazed a fire,
Sole street-lamp and the only sentinel.
    To other lands and nights my fancy turned—
To London first, and chiefly to your house,
The many-pillared and the well-beloved.
There yearning fancy lighted ; there again
In the upper room I lay, and heard far off
The unsleeping city murmur like a shell ;
The muffled tramp of the Museum guard
Once more went by me ; I beheld again
Lamps vainly brighten the dispeopled street ;
Again I longed for the returning morn,
The awaking traffic, the bestirring birds,

                    [1] Sidney Colvin.

The consentaneous trill of tiny song
That weaves round monumental cornices
A passing charm of beauty. Most of all,
For your light foot I wearied, and your knock
That was the glad réveillé of my day.

Lo, now, when to your task in the great house
At morning through the portico you pass,
One moment glance, where by the pillared wall
Far-voyaging island gods, begrimed with smoke,
Sit now unworshipped, the rude monument
Of faiths forgot and races undivined :
Sit now disconsolate, remembering well
The priest, the victim, and the songful crowd,
The blaze of the blue noon, and that huge voice,
Incessant, of the breakers on the shore.
As far as these from their ancestral shrine,
So far, so foreign, your divided friends
Wander, estranged in body, not in mind.

APEMAMA.

XXXVIII

THE HOUSE OF TEMBINOKA

[At my departure from the island of Apemama, for which you
will look in vain in most atlases, the King and I agreed, since
we both set up to be in the poetical way, that we should celebrate our separation in verse. Whether or not His Majesty has
been true to his bargain, the laggard posts of the Pacific may
perhaps inform me in six months, perhaps not before a year. The
following lines represent my part of the contract, and it is hoped,
by their pictures of strange manners, they may entertain a
civilised audience. Nothing throughout has been invented or
exaggerated; the lady herein referred to as the author's muse has
confined herself to stringing into rhyme facts or legends that I
saw or heard during two months' residence upon the island.—
R. L. S.]

ENVOI

Let us, who part like brothers, part like bards ;
And you in your tongue and measure, I in mine,
Our now division duly solemnise.

Unlike the strains, and yet the theme is one ;
The strains unlike, and how unlike their fate !
You to the blinding palace-yard shall call
The prefect of the singers, and to him,
Listening devout, your valedictory verse
Deliver ; he, his attribute fulfilled,
To the island chorus hand your measures on,
Wed now with harmony : so them, at last,
Night after night, in the open hall of dance,
Shall thirty matted men, to the clapped hand,
Intone and bray and bark.   Unfortunate !
Paper and print alone shall honour mine.

THE SONG

Let now the King his ear arouse
And toss the bosky ringlets from his brows,
The while, our bond to implement,
My muse relates and praises his descent.

i

Bride of the shark, her valour first I sing
Who on the lone seas quickened of a King.
She, from the shore and puny homes of men,
Beyond the climber's sea-discerning ken,
Swam, led by omens ; and devoid of fear,
Beheld her monstrous paramour draw near.
She gazed ; all round her to the heavenly pale,
The simple sea was void of isle or sail—
Sole overhead the unsparing sun was reared—
When the deep bubbled and the brute appeared.
But she, secure in the decrees of fate,
Made strong her bosom and received the mate :
And, men declare, from that marine embrace
Conceived the virtues of a stronger race.

II

Her stern descendant next I praise,
Survivor of a thousand frays :—

In the hall of tongues who ruled the throng ;
Led and was trusted by the strong ;
And when spears were in the wood,
Like a tower of vantage stood :—
Whom, not till seventy years had sped,
Unscarred of breast, erect of head,
Still light of step, still bright of look,
The hunter, Death, had overtook.

III

His sons, the brothers twain, I sing,
Of whom the elder reigned a King.
No Childeric he, yet much declined
From his rude sire's imperious mind,
Until his day came when he died,
He lived, he reigned, he versified.
But chiefly him I celebrate
That was the pillar of the state,
Ruled, wise of word and bold of mien,
The peaceful and the warlike scene ;
And played alike the leader's part
In lawful and unlawful art.
His soldiers with emboldened ears
Heard him laugh among the spears.
He could deduce from age to age
The web of island parentage ;
Best lay the rhyme, best lead the dance,
For any festal circumstance :
And fitly fashion oar and boat,
A palace or an armour coat.
None more availed than he to raise
The strong, suffumigating blaze
Or knot the wizard leaf : none more,
Upon the untrodden windward shore
Of the isle, beside the beating main,
To cure the sickly and constrain,
With muttered words and waving rods,
The gibbering and the whistling gods.

But he, though thus with hand and head
He ruled, commanded, charmed, and led,
And thus in virtue and in might
Towered to contemporary sight—
Still in fraternal faith and love,
Remained below to reach above,
Gave and obeyed the apt command,
Pilot and vassal of the land.

IV

My Tembinok' from men like these
Inherited his palaces,
His right to rule, his powers of mind;
His cocoa-islands sea-enshrined.
Stern bearer of the sword and whip,
A master passed in mastership,
He learned, without the spur of need,
To write, to cipher, and to read ;
From all that touch on his prone shore
Augments his treasury of lore,
Eager in age as erst in youth
To catch an art, to learn a truth,
To paint on the internal page
A clearer picture of the age.
His age, you say ? But ah, not so !
In his lone isle of long ago,
A royal Lady of Shalott,
Sea-sundered, he beholds it not ;
He only hears it far away.
The stress of equatorial day
He suffers ; he records the while
The vapid annals of the isle ;
Slaves bring him praise of his renown,
Or cackle of the palm-tree town ;
The rarer ship and the rare boat,
He marks ; and only hears remote,
Where thrones and fortunes rise and reel,
The thunder of the turning wheel.

V

For the unexpected tears he shed
At my departing, may his lion head
Not whiten, his revolving years
No fresh occasion minister of tears ;
At book or cards, at work or sport,
Him may the breeze across the palace court
For ever fan ; and swelling near
For ever the loud song divert his ear.

SCHOONER *Equator,* AT SEA.

XXXIX

THE WOODMAN

IN all the grove, nor stream nor bird
Nor aught beside my blows was heard,
And the woods wore their noonday dress—
The glory of their silentness.
From the island summit to the seas,
Trees mounted, and trees drooped, and trees
Groped upward in the gaps. The green
Inarboured talus and ravine
By fathoms. By the multitude
The rugged columns of the wood
And bunches of the branches stood :
Thick as a mob, deep as a sea,
And silent as eternity.

With lowered axe, with backward head,
Late from this scene my labourer fled,
And with a ravelled tale to tell,
Returned. Some denizen of hell,
Dead man or disinvested god,
Had close behind him peered and trod,
And triumphed when he turned to flee.
How different fell the lines with me !
Whose eye explored the dim arcade

L

Impatient of the uncoming shade—
Shy elf, or dryad pale and cold,
Or mystic lingerer from of old :
Vainly. The fair and stately things,
Impassive as departed kings,
All still in the wood's stillness stood,
And dumb. The rooted multitude
Nodded and brooded, bloomed and dreamed,
Unmeaning, undivined. It seemed
No other part, no hope, they knew,
Than clutch the earth and seek the blue.

  Mid vegetable king and priest
And stripling, I (the only beast)
Was at the beast's work, killing ; hewed
The stubborn roots across, bestrewed
The glebe with the dislustred leaves,
And bade the saplings fall in sheaves ;
Bursting across the tangled math
A ruin that I called a path,
A Golgotha that, later on,
When rains had watered, and suns shone,
And seeds enriched the place, should bear
And be called garden. Here and there,
I spied and plucked by the green hair
A foe more resolute to live,
The toothed and killing sensitive.
He, semi-conscious, fled the attack ;
He shrank and tucked his branches back ;
And straining by his anchor strand,
Captured and scratched the rooting hand.
I saw him crouch, I felt him bite ;
And straight my eyes were touched with sight.
I saw the wood for what it was :
The lost and the victorious cause,
The deadly battle pitched in line,
Saw silent weapons cross and shine :
Silent defeat, silent assault.
A battle and a burial vault.

Thick round me in the teeming mud
Briar and fern strove to the blood.
The hooked liana in his gin
Noosed his reluctant neighbours in:
There the green murderer throve and spread,
Upon his smothering victims fed,
And wantoned on his climbing coil.
Contending roots fought for the soil
Like frightened demons: with despair
Competing branches pushed for air.
Green conquerors from overhead
Bestrode the bodies of their dead:
The Cæsars of the silvan field,
Unused to fail, foredoomed to yield:
For in the groins of branches, lo!
The cancers of the orchid grow.

Silent as in the listed ring
Two chartered wrestlers strain and cling,
Dumb as by yellow Hooghly's side
The suffocating captives died:
So hushed the woodland warfare goes
Unceasing; and the silent foes
Grapple and smother, strain and clasp
Without a cry, without a gasp.
Here also sound thy fans, O God,
Here too thy banners move abroad:
Forest and city, sea and shore,
And the whole earth, thy threshing-floor!
The drums of war, the drums of peace,
Roll through our cities without cease,
And all the iron halls of life
Ring with the unremitting strife.

The common lot we scarce perceive.
Crowds perish, we nor mark nor grieve:
The bugle calls—we mourn a few!
What corporal's guard at Waterloo?

What scanty hundreds more or less
In the man-devouring Wilderness ?
What handful bled on Delhi ridge ?
—See, rather, London, on thy bridge
The pale battalions trample by,
Resolved to slay, resigned to die.
Count, rather, all the maimed and dead
In the unbrotherly war of bread.
See, rather, under sultrier skies
What vegetable Londons rise,
And teem, and suffer without sound.
Or in your tranquil garden ground,
Contented, in the falling gloom,
Saunter and see the roses bloom.
That these might live, what thousands died !
All day the cruel hoe was plied ;
The ambulance barrow rolled all day ;
Your wife, the tender, kind, and gay,
Donned her long gauntlets, caught the spud
And bathed in vegetable blood ;
And the long massacre now at end,
See ! where the lazy coils ascend,
See, where the bonfire sputters red
At even, for the innocent dead.

Why prate of peace ? when, warriors all,
We clank in harness into hall,
And ever bare upon the board
Lies the necessary sword.
In the green field or quiet street,
Besieged we sleep, beleaguered eat,
Labour by day and wake o' nights,
In war with rival appetites.
The rose on roses feeds ; the lark
On larks. The sedentary clerk
All morning with a diligent pen
Murders the babes of other men ;
And like the beasts of wood and park,
Protects his whelps, defends his den.

Unshamed the narrow aim I hold ;
I feed my sheep, patrol my fold ;
Breathe war on wolves and rival flocks,
A pious outlaw on the rocks
Of God and morning ; and when time
Shall bow, or rivals break me, climb
Where no undubbed civilian dares,
In my war harness, the loud stairs
Of honour ; and my conqueror
Hail me a warrior fallen in war.

VAILIMA.

XL

TROPIC RAIN

As the single pang of the blow, when the metal is mingled
     well,
Rings and lives and resounds in all the bounds of the
     bell :
So the thunder above spoke with a single tongue,
So in the heart of the mountain the sound of it rumbled
     and clung.

Sudden the thunder was drowned—quenched was the
     levin light—
And the angel-spirit of rain laughed out loud in the night.
Loud as the maddened river raves in the cloven glen,
Angel of rain ! you laughed and leaped on the roofs of
     men ;
And the sleepers sprang in their beds, and joyed and feared
     as you fell.
You struck, and my cabin quailed ; the roof of it roared
     like a bell,
You spoke, and at once the mountain shouted and shook
     with brooks.
You ceased, and the day returned, rosy, with virgin
     looks.

And methought that beauty and terror are only one, not
    two ;
And the world has room for love, and death, and thunder,
    and dew ;
And all the sinews of hell slumber in summer air ;
And the face of God is a rock, but the face of the rock is
    fair.
Beneficent streams of tears flow at the finger of pain ;
And out of the cloud that smites, beneficent rivers of
    rain.

VAILIMA.

XLI

AN END OF TRAVEL

LET now your soul in this substantial world
Some anchor strike. Be here the body moored :—
This spectacle immutably from now
The picture in your eye ; and when time strikes,
And the green scene goes on the instant blind—
The ultimate helpers, where your horse to-day
Conveyed you dreaming, bear your body dead.

VAILIMA.

XLII

WE uncommiserate pass into the night
From the loud banquet, and departing leave
A tremor in men's memories, faint and sweet
And frail as music. Features of our face,
The tones of the voice, the touch of the loved hand,
Perish and vanish, one by one, from earth :
Meanwhile, in the hall of song, the multitude
Applauds the new performer. One, perchance,
One ultimate survivor lingers on,
And smiles, and to his ancient heart recalls
The long forgotten. Ere the morrow die,
He too, returning, through the curtain comes,
And the new age forgets us and goes on.

XLIII

THE LAST SIGHT

ONCE more I saw him. In the lofty room,
Where oft with lights and company his tongue
Was trump to honest laughter, sate attired
A something in his likeness.—" Look ! " said one,
Unkindly kind, " look up, it is your boy ! "
And the dread changeling gazed on me in vain.

XLIV

SING me a song of a lad that is gone,
    Say, could that lad be I ?
Merry of soul he sailed on a day
    Over the sea to Skye.

Mull was astern, Rum on the port,
    Eigg on the starboard bow ;
Glory of youth glowed in his soul :
    Where is that glory now ?

Sing me a song of a lad that is gone,
    Say, could that lad be I ?
Merry of soul he sailed on a day
    Over the sea to Skye.

Give me again all that was there,
    Give me the sun that shone !
Give me the eyes, give me the soul,
    Give me the lad that's gone !

Sing me a song of a lad that is gone,
    Say, could that lad be I ?
Merry of soul he sailed on a day
    Over the sea to Skye.

Billow and breeze, islands and seas,
  Mountains of rain and sun,
All that was good, all that was fair,
  All that was me is gone.

XLV

TO S. R. CROCKETT

(IN REPLY TO A DEDICATION)

BLOWS the wind to-day, and the sun and the rain are
    flying,
  Blows the wind on the moors to-day and now,
Where about the graves of the martyrs the whaups are
    crying,
  My heart remembers how!

Grey recumbent tombs of the dead in desert places,
  Standing stones on the vacant wine-red moor,
Hills of sheep, and the homes of the silent vanquished
    races,
  And winds, austere and pure:

Be it granted me to behold you again in dying,
  Hills of home! and to hear again the call;
Hear about the graves of the martyrs the peewees crying,
  And hear no more at all.

VAILIMA.

XLVI

EVENSONG

THE embers of the day are red
Beyond the murky hill.
The kitchen smokes: the bed
In the darkling house is spread:
The great sky darkens overhead,
And the great woods are shrill.

So far have I been led,
Lord, by Thy will :
So far I have followed, Lord, and wondered
    still.
The breeze from the embalmèd land
Blows sudden toward the shore,
And claps my cottage door.
I hear the signal, Lord—I understand.
The night at Thy command
Comes. I will eat and sleep and will not
    question more.

VAILIMA.

MORAL EMBLEMS

& OTHER POEMS WRITTEN AND
ILLUSTRATED WITH WOODCUTS
BY ROBERT LOUIS STEVENSON
FIRST PRINTED AT THE DAVOS
PRESS BY LLOYD OSBOURNE

PREFATORY NOTE

By Lloyd Osbourne

IT is with some diffidence that I sit down at an age so mature that I cannot bring myself to name it, to write a preface to works I printed and published at twelve.

I would have the reader see a little boy living in a chalet on a Swiss mountain-side, overlooking a straggling village named Davos-Platz, where consumptives coming to get well more often died. It was winter; the sky-line was broken by frosty peaks; the hamlet—it was scarcely more then—lay huddled in the universal snow. Morning came late, and the sun set early. A still, silent, and icy night had an undue share of the round of hours, which at least it had the grace to mitigate by a myriad of shining stars.

The little boy thought it was a very jolly place. He loved the tobogganing, the skating, the snow-balling; loved the crisp, tingling air, and the woods full of Christmas trees, glittering with icicles. Nor with his toy theatre and printing-press was the indoor confinement ever irksome. He but dimly appreciated that his stepfather and mother were less happy in so favoured a spot. His mother's face was often anxious; sometimes he would find her crying. His stepfather, whom he idolised, was terribly thin, and even to childish eyes looked frail and spectral. The stepfather was an unsuccessful author named Robert Louis Stevenson, who would never have got along at all had it not been for his rich parents in Edinburgh. The little boy at his lessons in the room which they all shared grew used to hearing a sentence that struck at his heart. Perhaps it was the tone it was uttered in; perhaps the looks of discouragement and depression that went with it:

"Fanny, I shall have to write to my father."

It served to make the little boy very precocious about

173

money. In a family perennially short of it he learned its essentialness early. He knew, too, that he was a dreadfully expensive child. His stepfather paid forty pounds for his winter's tutoring, not to speak of an additional outlay on a dying Prussian officer who taught him German with the aid of a pocket-knife stuck down his throat to give him the right accent. It was with consternation that he once heard his stepfather say in a voice of tragedy : " Good heavens, Fanny, we are spending ten pounds a week on food alone ! "

The little boy, under the stress of this financial urgency, decided to go into business, finding a capital opening in the Hotel Belvidere where a hundred programmes were required weekly for the Saturday night concerts. A gentleman with a black beard, who was in charge of these arrangements, willingly offered to pay two francs fifty centimes for each set of programmes. The little boy was afraid of the gentleman with the black beard ; he was a formidable gentleman, with a formidable manner, and he was very exacting about spelling. The gentleman with the black beard attached an inordinate importance to spelling. The gentleman with the black beard was wholly unable to make allowances for the trifling mistakes that will occur in even the best-managed of printing-offices. If the little boy printed : " 'Twas in Trofolgar's Bay . . . sung by Mr. Edwin Smith," the black-bearded gentleman had no mercy in sending that poor little boy back to do it all over again. But he paid promptly—a severe man, but extremely honourable. There were charity-bazaars too, public invitations, announcements, letter-heads, all bringing grist to the mill. The *Elegy for some Lead Soldiers* was brought out, and sold for a penny. Once there was a colossal order for a thousand lottery tickets.

The little boy's ambitions soared. He wrote and printed a tiny book of eight pages, entitled *Black Canyon, or Life in the Far West*, in which he used all the " cuts " he had somehow accumulated with his type—the story conforming to the illustrations instead of the more commonplace way of the illustrations conforming to the text. This work can occasionally be picked up at one of Sotheby's auctions, and if you can get it for less than twenty-five pounds you are lucky—that is, if you are a collector and prize such things. It has risen to the dignity of " DAVOS BOOKLETS ; STEVENSONIANA ; EXCESSIVELY RARE." But its original price was sixpence, and its sale was immediate and gratifying. The little boy discovered that there was much more money to be made from one book than a dozen sets of programmes, and that without any black-bearded gentleman, either, to tweak his nose when errors crept in.

Louis, as the little boy always called his stepfather, with a familiarity that was much criticised by strangers, followed this publishing venture with absorbing interest. Then his own ambitions awakened, and one day, with an affected humility that was most embarrassing, he called at the office, and submitted a manuscript called, *Not I, and Other Poems*, which the firm of Osbourne and Co. gladly accepted on the spot. It was an instantaneous hit, selling out an entire edition of fifty copies.

The publisher was thrilled, and the author was equally jubilant, saying it was the only successful book he had ever written, and jingling his three francs of royalties with an air that made the little boy burst out laughing with delighted pride. In the ensuing enthusiasm another book was planned, and the first poem for it written.

" If only we could have illustrations," said the publisher longingly. But his " cuts " had all been used in *Black Canyon, or Life in the Far West*. Illustrations had to be put by as a dream impossible of fulfilment. No, not impossible ! Louis, who was a man of infinite resourcefulness (he could paint better theatre-scenes than any one could buy), said that he would try to carve some pictures on squares of fretwood. The word fretwood seems as unknown nowadays as the thing itself ; it was an extremely thin piece of board with which one was supposed to make works of art with the help of pasted-on patterns, an aggravating little saw, and the patience of Job. . . . Well, Louis cut out a small square of fretwood, and in a deeply-thoughtful manner applied himself to the task. He had only a pocket-knife ; real tools came later ; but he was impelled by a will to win that carried all before it.

After an afternoon of almost suffocating excitement— for the publisher—he completed the engraving that accompanies the poem : " Reader, your soul upraise to see." But it had yet to be mounted on a wooden block in order to raise it to the exact level of the type. At last this was done. A proof was run off. But the impression was unequal. Oh the disappointment ! Author and publisher gazed at each other in misery. But woman's wit came to the rescue. Why not build it up with cigarette-papers ? " Bravo, Fanny ! " The author set to work, deftly and skilfully. Then more proofs, more cigarette-papers, more running up and down stairs to the little boy's room, which in temperature hovered about zero. But what was temperature ? The thing was a success. The little boy, entranced beyond measure, printed copy after copy, from the sheer pleasure of seeing the wet ink magically reproducing the block.

The next day the little boy was sent to a dying Swiss— half the population of Davos were coughing away the remnants of life—who lived with his poverty-stricken family in one room, earning their bread by carving bears. A model block was shown him. Could he produce a dozen exactly like it, but in a wood without any grain ? The dying Swiss said he could, leaving his bear forthwith, and applying himself to the task. The pinched-face children looked on amazed ; the little print of " Reader, your soul upraise to see " was passed from hand to hand with exclamations of astonishment. The dying Swiss gave the little boy the blocks, beautifully and faultlessly finished. Would the little boy care to buy a bear ? No, the little boy didn't. He scurried home through the snow with the precious blocks.

Thus *Moral Emblems* came out ; ninety copies, price sixpence. Its reception might almost be called sensational. Wealthy people in the Hotel Belvidere bought as many as three copies apiece. Friends in England wrote back for more. Meanwhile the splendid artist was assiduously busy. He worked like a beaver, saying that it was the best relaxation he had ever found. The little boy once over-heard him confiding to a visitor : " I cannot tell you what a godsend these silly blocks have been to me. When I can write no more, and read no more, and think no more, I can pass whole hours engraving these blocks in blissful contentment." These may not have been the actual words, but such at least was their sense.

Thus the second *Moral Emblems* came out ; ninety copies, price ninepence. The public welcomed it as heartily as the first, the little boy becoming so prosperous that he accu-mulated upwards of five pounds. But let it never be said that he spurned the humble mainstay of his beginnings. He printed the weekly programmes as usual, and bore the exactions of the black-bearded gentleman with fortitude. When he made such a trifling mistake, for instance, as " The Harp that Once Through Tara's Hells," he dutifully climbed the hill to his freezing room, and ran off a whole fresh set. Two francs fifty was two francs fifty. Every business man appreciates the comfort of a small regular order which can be counted on like the clock.

But one day there was no black-bearded gentleman. " Oh, he was dead. Had had a hemorrhage three days before and had died." I don't know whether the little boy mourned for him particularly, but it was a shock to lose that two francs fifty centimes. The little boy was worried until he found a lady who had substituted herself for the gentleman with the black beard. She was a very kind lady ; you could print anything for that lady, and " get away with it," as Americans say. But she was frolic-some and lacked poise ; she was vague about appointments, and had a disheartening way of saying : " Oh, bother," when the little boy appeared ; she would insist on kissing him amid circumstances of the most odious publicity ; was so abased a creature besides, that she often marred the programmes by making pen-and-ink corrections. In contrast, the little boy looked back on the black-bearded gentleman almost with regret.

Two winters were thus occupied, with incidental

M

education that seemed far less important. The Prussian officer had fortunately died, releasing the little boy from any further study of German. All that he retains of it to-day is the taste of that pocket-knife, and of the Prussian officer's thumb. Then he was sent to a boarding-school in England, or, to be precise, to a tutor who had half a dozen resident pupils. Time passed; publishing became a memory. Then a long summer holiday found the little boy, now much grown and matured, reunited with his family in Kingussie. The printing-press was there, and business was resumed with enthusiasm. The stepfather, who had made much more progress with engraving than the boy had with Latin, had the blocks and poems all ready for *The Graver and the Pen*.

But the printing-press broke down; and after an interval of despair and unavailing attempts to repair it, an amiable old man was found who had a press of his own behind a microscopic general shop. Here *The Graver and the Pen* was printed with what now seems an almost regrettable perfection. The amiable old man was altogether too amiable. He would insist on doing far too much himself, though he had been merely paid a trifling rent for the use of the press. An edition of a hundred copies was printed, of which almost none were sold. The little boy had grown such a big boy that he was ashamed of tradesmanship. He had passed the age when he could take sixpences and ninepences with ease from strangers. New standards were imperceptibly forming, and it pleased him better to see his stepfather give away *The Graver and the Pen* to those worthy of so signal an honour.

In fact, *The Graver and the Pen* was the last enterprise of Osbourne and Co. *The Pirate and the Apothecary* was projected; three superb illustrations were engraved for it; yet it never saw more light than the typewriter afforded. *The Builder's Doom* has remained in manuscript until the present time. No illustrations were either drawn or engraved for it. It marked the final decline of a once flourishing business, which in its day had given so much laughter to many people sadly in need of it.   L. O.

NOT I
AND OTHER POEMS

NOT I

I

Some like drink
In a pint pot,
Some like to think;
    Some not.

Strong Dutch cheese,
Old Kentucky rye,
Some like these;
    Not I.

Some like Poe,
And others like Scott,
Some like Mrs. Stowe;
    Some not.

Some like to laugh,
Some like to cry,
Some like chaff;
    Not I.

II

Here, perfect to a wish
We offer, not a dish,
    But just the platter:
A book that's not a book,
A pamphlet in the look
    But not the matter.

I own in disarray ;
As to the flowers of May
    The frosts of Winter ;
To my poetic rage,
The smallness of the page
    And of the printer.

III

As seamen on the seas
With song and dance descry
Adown the morning breeze
An islet in the sky :
In Araby the dry,
As o'er the sandy plain
The panting camels cry
To smell the coming rain :

So all things over earth
A common law obey,
And rarity and worth
Pass, arm in arm, away ;
And even so, to-day,
The printer and the bard,
In pressless Davos, pray
Their sixpenny reward.

IV

The pamphlet here presented
Was planned and printed by
A printer unindented,
A bard whom all decry.

The author and the printer,
With various kinds of skill,

Concocted it in Winter
At Davos on the Hill.

They burned the nightly taper;
But now the work is ripe—
Observe the costly paper,
Remark the perfect type!

MORAL EMBLEMS

I

I

SEE how the children in the print
Bound on the book to see what's in't!
O, like these pretty babes, may you
Seize and *apply* this volume too!
And while your eye upon the cuts
With harmless ardour opes and shuts,
Reader, may your immortal mind
To their sage lessons not be blind.

II

READER, your soul upraise to see,
In yon fair cut designed by me,
The pauper by the highway-side
Vainly soliciting from pride.
Mark how the Beau with easy air
Contemns the anxious rustic's prayer,
And, casting a disdainful eye,
Goes gaily gallivanting by.
He from the poor averts his head . . .
He will regret it when he's dead.

III

A PEAK IN DARIEN

BROAD-GAZING on untrodden lands,
See where adventurous Cortez stands;
While in the heavens above his head
The Eagle seeks its daily bread.
How aptly fact to fact replies:
Heroes and eagles, hills and skies.
Ye, who contemn the fatted slave,
Look on this emblem and be brave.

IV

SEE in the print how, moved by whim,
Trumpeting Jumbo, great and grim,
Adjusts his trunk, like a cravat,
To noose that individual's hat.
The sacred Ibis in the distance
Joys to observe his bold resistance.

V

MARK, printed on the opposing page,
The unfortunate effects of rage.
A man (who might be you or me)
Hurls another into the sea.
Poor soul, his unreflecting act
His future joys will much contract,
And he will spoil his evening toddy
By dwelling on that mangled body.

MORAL EMBLEMS

II

I

WITH storms a-weather, rocks a-lee,
The dancing skiff puts forth to sea.
The lone dissenter in the blast
Recoils before the sight aghast.
But she, although the heavens be black,
Holds on upon the starboard tack.
For why? although to-day she sink,
Still safe she sails in printer's ink,
And though to-day the seamen drown,
My cut shall hand their memory down.

II

THE careful angler chose his nook
At morning by the lilied brook,
And all the noon his rod he plied
By that romantic riverside.
Soon as the evening hours decline
Tranquilly he'll return to dine,
And, breathing forth a pious wish,
Will cram his belly full of fish.

III

THE Abbot for a walk went out,
A wealthy cleric, very stout,
And Robin has that Abbot stuck
As the red hunter spears the buck.
The djavel or the javelin
Has, you observe, gone bravely in,
And you may hear that weapon whack
Bang through the middle of his back.
Hence we may learn that abbots should
Never go walking in a wood.

IV

THE frozen peaks he once explored,
But now he's dead and by the board.
How better far at home to have stayed
Attended by the parlour maid,
And warmed his knees before the fire
Until the hour when folks retire !
So, if you would be spared to friends,
Do nothing but for business ends.

V

INDUSTRIOUS pirate ! see him sweep
The lonely bosom of the deep,
And daily the horizon scan
From Hatteras or Matapan.
Be sure, before that pirate's old,
He will have made a pot of gold,
And will retire from all his labours
And be respected by his neighbours.
You also scan your life's horizon
For all that you can clap your eyes on.

A MARTIAL ELEGY FOR SOME
LEAD SOLDIERS

A MARTIAL ELEGY FOR SOME LEAD SOLDIERS

For certain soldiers lately dead
Our reverent dirge shall here be said.
Them, when their martial leader called,
No dread preparative appalled;
But leaden-hearted, leaden-heeled,
I marked them steadfast in the field.
Death grimly sided with the foe,
And smote each leaden hero low.
Proudly they perished one by one:
The dread Pea-cannon's work was done!
O not for them the tears we shed,
Consigned to their congenial lead;
But while unmoved their sleep they take,
We mourn for their dear Captain's sake,
For their dear Captain, who shall smart
Both in his pocket and his heart,
Who saw his heroes shed their gore,
And lacked a shilling to buy more!

THE GRAVER AND THE PEN:

OR,

SCENES FROM NATURE, WITH
APPROPRIATE VERSES

I

PROEM

UNLIKE the common run of men,
  I wield a double power to please,
And use the GRAVER and the PEN
  With equal aptitude and ease.

I move with that illustrious crew,
  The ambidextrous Kings of Art;
And every mortal thing I do
  Brings ringing money in the mart

Hence, in the morning hour, the mead,
  The forest and the stream perceive
Me wandering as the muses lead—
  Or back returning in the eve.

Two muses like two maiden aunts,
  The engraving and the singing muse,
Follow, through all my favourite haunts,
  My devious traces in the dews.

To guide and cheer me, each attends;
  Each speeds my rapid task along;
One to my cuts her ardour lends,
  One breathes her magic in my song.

II

THE PRECARIOUS MILL

ALONE above the stream it stands,
    Above the iron hill,
The topsy-turvy, tumble-down,
    Yet habitable mill.

Still as the ringing saws advance
    To slice the humming deal,
All day the pallid miller hears
    The thunder of the wheel.

He hears the river plunge and roar
    As roars the angry mob ;
He feels the solid building quake,
    The trusty timbers throb.

All night beside the fire he cowers :
    He hears the rafters jar :
O why is he not in a proper house
    As decent people are !

The floors are all aslant, he sees,
    The doors are all a-jam ;
And from the hook above his head
    All crooked swings the ham.

" Alas," he cries and shakes his head,
    " I see by every sign,
There soon will be the deuce to pay,
    With this estate of mine."

III

THE DISPUTATIOUS PINES

THE first pine to the second said :
" My leaves are black, my branches red ;
I stand upon this moor of mine,
A hoar, unconquerable pine."

The second sniffed and answered : " Pooh !
I am as good a pine as you."

" Discourteous tree," the first replied,
" The tempest in my boughs had cried,
The hunter slumbered in my shade,
A hundred years ere you were made."

The second smiled as he returned :
" I shall be here when you are burned."

So far dissension ruled the pair,
Each turned on each a frowning air,
When flickering from the bank anigh,
A flight of martens met their eye.
Sometime their course they watched ; and then
They nodded off to sleep again.

IV

THE TRAMPS

Now long enough had day endured,
Or King Apollo Palinured,
Seaward he steers his panting team,
And casts on earth his latest gleam.

But see ! the Tramps with jaded eye
Their destined provinces espy.
Long through the hills their way they took,
Long camped beside the mountain brook ;
'Tis over ; now with rising hope
They pause upon the downward slope,
And as their aching bones they rest,
Their anxious captain scans the west.

So paused Alaric on the Alps
And ciphered up the Roman scalps.

V

THE FOOLHARDY GEOGRAPHER

THE howling desert miles around,
The tinkling brook the only sound—
Wearied with all his toils and feats,
The traveller dines on potted meats;
On potted meats and princely wines,
Not wisely but too well he dines.

The brindled Tiger loud may roar,
High may the hovering Vulture soar;
Alas! regardless of them all,
Soon shall the empurpled glutton sprawl—
Soon, in the desert's hushed repose,
Shall trumpet tidings through his nose!
Alack, unwise! that nasal song
Shall be the Ounce's dinner-gong!

A blemish in the cut appears;
Alas! it cost both blood and tears.
The glancing graver swerved aside,
Fast flowed the artist's vital tide!
And now the apologetic bard
Demands indulgence for his pard!

VI

THE ANGLER AND THE CLOWN

THE echoing bridge you here may see,
The pouring lynn, the waving tree,
The eager angler fresh from town—
Above, the contumelious clown.
The angler plies his line and rod,
The clodpole stands with many a nod,—
With many a nod and many a grin,
He sees him cast his engine in.

" What have you caught ? " the peasant cries.

" Nothing as yet," the Fool replies.

THE ANGLER AND THE CLOWN

MORAL TALES

THE PIRATE AND THE APOTHECARY : SCENE THE FIRST

I

ROBIN AND BEN : OR, THE PIRATE AND THE APOTHECARY

COME, lend me an attentive ear
A startling moral tale to hear,
Of Pirate Rob and Chemist Ben,
And different destinies of men.

Deep in the greenest of the vales
That nestle near the coast of Wales,
The heaving main but just in view,
Robin and Ben together grew,
Together worked and played the fool,
Together shunned the Sunday school,
And pulled each other's youthful noses
Around the cots, among the roses.

Together but unlike they grew ;
Robin was rough, and through and through
Bold, inconsiderate, and manly,
Like some historic Bruce or Stanley.
Ben had a mean and servile soul,
He robbed not, though he often stole ;
He sang on Sunday in the choir,
And tamely capped the passing Squire.

At length, intolerant of trammels—
Wild as the wild Bithynian camels,
Wild as the wild sea-eagles—Bob
His widowed dam contrives to rob,
And thus with great originality
Effectuates his personality.

Thenceforth his terror-haunted flight
He follows through the starry night;
And with the early morning breeze,
Behold him on the azure seas.
The master of a trading dandy
Hires Robin for a go of brandy;
And all the happy hills of home
Vanish beyond the fields of foam.

Ben, meanwhile, like a tin reflector,
Attended on the worthy rector;
Opened his eyes and held his breath,
And flattered to the point of death;
And was at last, by that good fairy,
Apprenticed to the Apothecary.

So Ben, while Robin chose to roam,
A rising chemist was at home,
Tended his shop with learnéd air,
Watered his drugs and oiled his hair,
And gave advice to the unwary,
Like any sleek apothecary.

Meanwhile upon the deep afar
Robin the brave was waging war,
With other tarry desperadoes
About the latitude of Barbadoes.
He knew no touch of craven fear;
His voice was thunder in the cheer;
First, from the main-to'-gallan' high,
The skulking merchantmen to spy—

The first to bound upon the deck,
The last to leave the sinking wreck.
His hand was steel, his word was law,
His mates regarded him with awe.
No pirate in the whole profession
Held a more honourable position.

At length, from years of anxious toil,
Bold Robin seeks his native soil ;
Wisely arranges his affairs,
And to his native dale repairs.
The Bristol *Swallow* sets him down
Beside the well-remembered town.
He sighs, he spits, he marks the scene,
Proudly he treads the village green ;
And, free from pettiness and rancour,
Takes lodgings at the " Crown and Anchor."

Strange, when a man so great and good
Once more in his home-country stood,
Strange that the sordid clowns should show
A dull desire to have him go.
His clinging breeks, his tarry hat,
The way he swore, the way he spat,
A certain quality of manner,
Alarming like the pirate's banner—
Something that did not seem to suit all—
Something, O call it bluff, not brutal—
Something at least, howe'er it's called,
Made Robin generally black-balled.

His soul was wounded ; proud and glum,
Alone he sat and swigged his rum,
And took a great distaste to men
Till he encountered Chemist Ben.
Bright was the hour and bright the day
That threw them in each other's way ;
Glad were their mutual salutations,
Long their respective revelations.
Before the inn in sultry weather
They talked of this and that together
Ben told the tale of his indentures,
And Rob narrated his adventures.
Last, as the point of greatest weight,
The pair contrasted their estate,

THE PIRATE AND THE APOTHECARY : SCENE THE SECOND

And Robin, like a boastful sailor,
Despised the other for a tailor.

" See," he remarked, " with envy see
A man with such a fist as me !
Bearded and ringed, and big, and brown,
I sit and toss the stingo down.
Hear the gold jingle in my bag—
All won beneath the Jolly Flag ! "

Ben moralised and shook his head :
" You wanderers earn and eat your bread.
The foe is found, beats or is beaten,
And either how, the wage is eaten.
And after all your pully-hauly
Your proceeds look uncommon small-ly.
You had done better here to tarry
Apprentice to the Apothecary.
The silent pirates of the shore
Eat and sleep soft, and pocket more
Than any red, robustious ranger
Who picks his farthings hot from danger.
You clank your guineas on the board ;
Mine are with several bankers stored.
You reckon riches on your digits,
You dash in chase of Sals and Bridgets,
You drink and risk delirium tremens,
Your whole estate a common seaman's !
Regard your friend and school companion,
Soon to be wed to Miss Trevanion
(Smooth, honourable, fat and flowery,
With Heaven knows how much land in
    dowry),
Look at me—Am I in good case ?
Look at my hands, look at my face ;
Look at the cloth of my apparel ;
Try me and test me, lock and barrel ;
And own, to give the devil his due,
I have made more of life than you.

THE PIRATE AND THE APOTHECARY : SCENE THE THIRD

Yet I nor sought nor risked a life ;
I shudder at an open knife ;
The perilous seas I still avoided
And stuck to land whate'er betided.
I had no gold, no marble quarry,
I was a poor apothecary,
Yet here I stand, at thirty-eight,
A man of an assured estate."

" Well," answered Robin—" well, and how ? "

The smiling chemist tapped his brow.
" Rob," he replied, " this throbbing brain
Still worked and hankered after gain ;
By day and night, to work my will,
It pounded like a powder mill ;
And marking how the world went round
A theory of theft it found.
Here is the key to right and wrong :
Steal little but steal all day long ;
And this invaluable plan
Marks what is called the Honest Man.
When first I served with Doctor Pill,
My hand was ever in the till ;
Now that I am myself a master
My gains come softer still and faster.
As thus : on Wednesday, a maid
Came to me in the way of trade ;
Her mother, an old farmer's wife,
Required a drug to save her life.
' At once, my dear, at once,' I said,
Patted the child upon the head,
Bade her be still a loving daughter,—
And filled the bottle up with water."

" Well, and the mother ? " Robin cried.

" O, she ! " said Ben, " I think she died."

" Battle and blood, death and disease,
Upon the tainted Tropic seas—
The attendant sharks that chew the cud—
The abhorred scuppers spouting blood—
The untended dead, the Tropic sun—
The thunder of the murderous gun—
The cut-throat crew—the Captain's curse—
The tempest blustering worse and worse—
These have I known and these can stand,
But you—I settle out of hand ! "

Out flashed the cutlass, down went Ben,
Dead and rotten, there and then.

II

THE BUILDER'S DOOM

IN eighteen-twenty Deacon Thin
Feu'd the land and fenced it in,
And laid his broad foundations down
About a furlong out of town.

Early and late the work went on.
The carts were toiling ere the dawn ;
The mason whistled, the hodman sang ;
Early and late the trowels rang ;
And Thin himself came day by day
To push the work in every way.
An artful builder, patent king
Of all the local building ring,
Who was there like him in the quarter
For mortifying brick and mortar,
Or pocketing the odd piastre
By substituting lath and plaster ?
With plan and two-foot rule in hand.
He by the foreman took his stand,

With boisterous voice, with eagle glance
To stamp upon extravagance.
For thrift of bricks and greed of guilders,
He was the Buonaparte of Builders.

The foreman, a desponding creature,
Demurred to here and there a feature :
" For surely, sir—with your permeesion—
Bricks here, sir, in the main parteetion. . . . "

The builder goggled, gulped and stared,
The foreman's services were spared.
Thin would not count among his minions
A man of Wesleyan opinions.

" Money is money," so he said.
" Crescents are crescents, trade is trade.
Pharaohs and emperors in their seasons
Built, I believe, for different reasons—
Charity, glory, piety, pride—
To pay the men, to please a bride,
To use their stone, to spite their neighbours,
Not for a profit on their labours.
They built to edify or bewilder ;
I build because I am a builder.
Crescent and street and square I build,
Plaster and paint and carve and gild.
Around the city see them stand,
These triumphs of my shaping hand,
With bulging walls, with sinking floors,
With shut, impracticable doors,
Fickle and frail in every part,
And rotten to their inmost heart.
There shall the simple tenant find
Death in the falling window-blind,
Death in the pipe, death in the faucet,
Death in the deadly water-closet !
A day is set for all to die :
Caveat emptor ! what care I ? "

As to Amphion's tuneful kit
Thebes rose, with towers encircling it ;
As to the Mage's brandished wand
A spiry palace clove the sand ;
To Thin's indomitable financing,
That phantom crescent kept advancing.
When first the brazen bells of churches
Called clerk and parson to their perches,
The worshippers of every sect
Already viewed it with respect ;
A second Sunday had not gone
Before the roof was rattled on :
And when the fourth was there, behold
The crescent finished, painted, sold !

The stars proceeded in their courses,
Nature with her subversive forces,
Time, too, the iron-toothed and sinewed,
And the edacious years continued.
Thrones rose and fell ; and still the crescent,
Unsanative and now senescent,
A plastered skeleton of lath,
Looked forward to a day of wrath.
In the dead night, the groaning timber
Would jar upon the ear of slumber,
And, like Dodona's talking oak,
Of oracles and judgments spoke.
When to the music fingered well
The feet of children lightly fell,
The sire, who dozed by the decanters,
Started, and dreamed of misadventures.
The rotten brick decayed to dust ;
The iron was consumed by rust ;
Each tabid and perverted mansion
Hung in the article of declension.

So forty, fifty, sixty passed ;
Until, when seventy came at last,
The occupant of number three

Called friends to hold a jubilee.
Wild was the night ; the charging rack
Had forced the moon upon her back ;
The wind piped up a naval ditty ;
And the lamps winked through all the city.
Before that house, where lights were shining,
Corpulent feeders, grossly dining,
And jolly clamour, hum and rattle,
Fairly outvoiced the tempest's battle.
As still his moistened lip he fingered,
The envious policeman lingered ;
While far the infernal tempest sped,
And shook the country folks in bed,
And tore the trees and tossed the ships,
He lingered and he licked his lips.
Lo, from within, a hush ! the host
Briefly expressed the evening's toast ;
And lo, before the lips were dry,
The Deacon rising to reply !
" Here in this house which once I built,
Papered and painted, carved and gilt,
And out of which, to my content,
I netted seventy-five per cent.;
Here at this board of jolly neighbours,
I reap the credit of my labours.
These were the days—I will say more—
These were the grand old days of yore !
The builder laboured day and night ;
He watched that every brick was right :
The decent men their utmost did ;
And the house rose—a pyramid !
These were the days, our provost knows,
When forty streets and crescents rose,
The fruits of my creative noddle,
All more or less upon a model,
Neat and commodious, cheap and dry,
A perfect pleasure to the eye !
I found this quite a country quarter ;
I leave it solid lath and mortar.

In all, I was the single actor—
And am this city's benefactor !
Since then, alas ! both thing and name,
Shoddy across the ocean came—
Shoddy that can the eye bewilder
And makes me blush to meet a builder !
Had this good house, in frame or fixture,
Been tempered by the least admixture
Of that discreditable shoddy,
Should we to-day compound our toddy,
Or gaily marry song and laughter
Below its sempiternal rafter ?
Not so ! " the Deacon cried.

                 The mansion
Had marked his fatuous expansion.
The years were full, the house was fated,
The rotten structure crepitated !

A moment, and the silent guests
Sat pallid as their dinner vests.
A moment more and, root and branch,
That mansion fell in avalanche,
Story on story, floor on floor,
Roof, wall and window, joist and door,
Dead weight of damnable disaster,
A cataclysm of lath and plaster.

Siloam did not choose a sinner—
All were not builders at the dinner.

Printed in Great Britain by
The Greycaine Book Manufacturing Company Limited, Watford.
100.927